Jim Montgomery

GRAPHIC ARTS

GRAPHIC ARTS

Darvey E. Carlsen
Associate Professor
University of California
Santa Barbara

Chas. A. Bennett Co., Inc.
Peoria, Illinois

4

CONTENTS

THE PLAN OF THIS BOOK

THIS TEXT covers the basic fundamentals in each of the activity areas in general graphic arts. Emphasis has been placed on the manipulative operations which are illustrated in their proper sequence in doing a simple job from beginning to completion. Since every job is made up of one or more operations, the typical jobs which have been illustrated and explained in each area provide an opportunity to better understand the operations and to visualize the various steps in their proper order.

After instruction has been given in an area, it will be most helpful to read the explanation and study the illustrations dealing with this area. Since not all students will be able to work in the same area at the same time, it will be necessary for many of you to perform the operations several days after the demonstration. In this case, review the material which deals with your problem just before you start work on it.

Although your job may not be identical to the job illustrated, keep in mind that the operations will be the same and the sequence in which the operations are performed will also be the same as illustrated.

It is important to follow the sequence outlined because it gives a logical order in doing a job, and it is also easier to remember a procedure when it is performed in the same order each time.

We all like to do the things we know how to do, and you will enjoy your work in graphic arts in proportion to how well you understand and know what you are doing.

At the end of each chapter you will find test questions. This provides an opportunity to test yourself. You will also find it to be a helpful study guide.

The selected bibliography provides a list of suggested references for each area. This will be particularly helpful after you understand the fundamentals and are prepared for advanced work in each area.

GRAPHIC ARTS is a term widely used in industry, as well as in education, to describe printing and allied crafts. "Printing" has a restrictive connotation; graphic arts is a broader term, generally interpreted to include all activities closely allied to the printing and publishing field. Graphic arts activities in industrial arts classes are being broadened to give a better cross-section of the industry as well as providing experiences for popular and worthwhile leisure-time hobbies.

As one of the ten leading industries in the United States, graphic arts ranks high in number of employees, value of product, number of establishments, and the use of its products in daily living.

The four common methods of reproducing printed materials are relief printing, planographic printing, intaglio printing, and stencil printing. Paper making, bookbinding, and photography may be combined with one or more of the above printing processes.

Relief printing, commonly referred to as letterpress printing in the industry, means to reproduce the printed piece from type or engravings which have been made in relief. A piece of type, for example, has a printing surface which is in relief from the body of the type character. When the surface has been inked, the design may be transferred to paper by applying pressure. The *rubber stamp,* familiar to most everyone, is a typical relief printing medium.

Planographic printing refers to reproductions made from a plate on which the image and the non-printing surface are on the same plane. Ink is transferred to a rubber surface, from which the actual printing is done. This process is commonly referred to as *lithographic printing,* offset, photo-offset, and lithography. The Greek word lithos means stone, which was used by early artisans.

Intaglio printing is the reverse of relief printing. The image is actually below the surface of the printing plate. After ink is applied to the plate, the plate is wiped, leaving a deposit of ink in the depressions. The ink is transferred to paper by placing pressure against the sheet in contact with the plate. The intaglio printing process is commonly referred to in the industry as *gravure printing.* This is a more specialized method of reproduction and is therefore confined to a limited number of plants. In the school laboratory, this method is well adapted to making dry point plates and prints.

Certain kinds of *stencil printing* are perhaps the best understood printing process now being used, namely *mimeograph duplicating*. The mimeograph makes duplicate copies inexpensively and quickly. A wax coating on the stencil is penetrated by either a typewriter or stylus. When the stencil is stretched tightly over a perforated ink drum, ink seeps through the open area of the stencil onto the paper when the cylinder is rotated. This machine, although a method of reproducing copy, is generally classified as an office machine rather than equipment associated with graphic arts.

Silk screen printing is one of the newest and most rapidly growing and expanding member of the graphic arts processes. In this process, stencils may be either hand cut or made photographically; they are attached to silk stretched tightly across a frame. Ink is then forced through the open areas of the stencil onto the paper by means of a squeegee. Very simple equipment for short runs, or very elaborate equipment for mass production runs, may be employed. The process is not only flexible with respect to equipment, but it is also very versatile for printing on various types of surfaces and materials, as well as size or area that may be printed at one time. New advances in fabrics, types of screens, the application of photographic principles, and equipment have stimulated its growth in recent years.

Bookbinding and allied bindery operations are closely associated with all printing processes. Bookbinding, like silk screen printing, may be done with very simple or with complex expensive machinery typical of automation developed to a high degree. Hand binding is an art as old as printing from movable type. Hand binding of short runs, such as in binding volumes of magazines for their preservation, and the repair of books are still important phases of the industry as well as popular leisure-time activities.

Paper making preceded printing from movable type and might be said to have made it possible for the graphic arts to develop into one of the world's greatest industries. Paper making has not only kept pace with other areas but has often been a leader in new developments. Smooth papers preceded the design of fine line, sharply defined type. Innovations in the coating of paper to make it smooth for quality reproduction of photographs preceded the growth of picture magazines, just as the invention of the Fourdrinier paper-making machine in 1798 preceded mass-produced newspapers. Handmade paper is frequently used by hobbyists for their personal greeting cards. Graphic arts students learn the basic principles of the manufacture of paper by trying the hand process, which also gives an opportunity for unique applications of color and texture.

Photography is an ever-expanding area in graphic arts. Its innovations are constantly providing new applications in all forms of reproduction.

Graphic arts activities provide unlimited opportunities to integrate other school subjects with a laboratory experience. English, mathematics, art, and science are all important in one or more phases of the graphics.

In the preparation of copy, the student has an opportunity to make a direct application of the fundamentals of English. In type composition, the student must be alert to spelling, punctuation, capitalization, and word division. Proofreading demands constant attention to detail and uniformity in composition.

Stock cutting, estimating quantities of stock, as well as an application of the printers system of measure re-

9

quire every student to make application of the fundamentals of mathematics.

Design and layout require the application of the principles of art and provide an opportunity for self-expression in several media of reproduction.

Cooperative projects with other school classes are not only practical but assist in making all subjects more meaningful. For example, a calendar devoting one page to each month in the year might be worked out. The English class might prepare the copy, including an appropriate quotation or motto for each month in the year. The art class might prepare an appropriate linoleum block design for each month; and the graphic arts class might contribute to the project by doing the type composition, proofreading, presswork, and binding. Often the entire project may be carried out in a graphic arts class, if coordinating three classes in one situation is not practical.

Purpose of This Text

The purpose of this text is to provide in one volume a summary explanation of the procedures and techniques in basic graphic arts activities. The prime objective has been to make the introduction simple and easy to understand for the beginner in all of the basic areas.

Activities include those considered desirable by leaders in graphic arts and education. In most instances, trade practice is presented; where deviations have been made, the purpose has been to simplify the operation to make it easier for the immature learner, keeping in mind that the objective is exploratory, and that the learner is not expected to develop a high degree of skill through repetition or mass-production techniques.

Emphasis is placed upon manipulative aspects in the various operations because there is a need for instructional aids to supplement class demonstrations. In unit graphic arts, as well as general industrial arts work areas, it is necessary for students to work in several different media at the same time. Since it is not always possible for you to perform manipulative operations immediately following a class demonstration, a ready reference is most helpful in reviewing the demonstration immediately before performance of the operations.

This does not minimize the need, or the desirability, for instructional materials and aids in the realm of related information. Limitations here are to keep the author's presentation within reasonable bounds.

Shop libraries, films, field trips, and lectures are all desirable.

2-1. Line gauge

Chapter 2

EVER SINCE the invention of movable type by Johann Gutenberg in 1439, the volume of work printed from type and relief plates has enjoyed constant growth in volume and quality.

Letterpress printing, which is a relief printing process, is the medium used to print most newspapers, magazines, a wide variety of books, and simpler printed forms.

Composition

Type may be composed by hand or by machine. Since one size and style of type costs several hundred dollars more to install on a machine than the same size and style of type for hand composition, it is natural that a considerable amount of type is still composed by hand.

In large printing plants, the volume of composition warrants a large selection of type styles which can be composed by machine, while in the smaller plants, styles of type which can be composed by machine are restricted. In commercial printing plants, hand composition is usually limited to single lines in the larger sizes and styles of type which are used only for display heads and labels.

The same principles, and many of the same operations, are common to both hand and machine composition. The beginning student in graphic arts, like the apprentice in the printing trade, first sets type by hand to become familiar with the fundamentals.

The Point System

The printers system of measurement is unique. Because small units are being dealt with so frequently, the inch is divided into seventy-two parts, each part called a point. The other unit of measurement is called a pica, which is equal to twelve points. Thus there are six picas in one inch.

The *printers rule* (2-1), which is graduated in picas and half picas, is called a line gauge. It is used for making measurements in the composition of type forms. See page 10.

Type Sizes

Type sizes, today, are specified in points. Commonly used type sizes in composition are 6, 8, 10, 12, 14, 18, 24, 30, 36, 42, 48, 60, and 72 point. Sizes larger than 72 point are now usually made of wood and their size is specified in lines. A line is equal to 1 pica or 12 points. In other words, 12 line wood type would be 12 picas in height.

Parts of Type

The important parts of a piece of type are the face, the body, the nick and the feet.

The face is the part that prints; the body supports the face; and the feet are that on which the type stands. The nick indicates how the letters

11

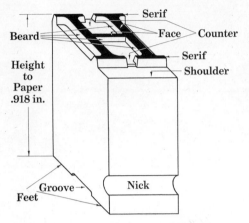

2-2. Parts of a piece of type

fornia job case, the "news" case was in vogue. The capital letters were placed in a case above the small letters in a slanted position. The old "news" cases are credited with being the origin of the terms "upper case" for the capital letters and "lower case" for the small letters.

The California job case is divided into three sections (2-3). The left two thirds of the case is devoted to lower case letters, figures, punctuation marks and spaces. The right third of the case is devoted to capital letters, dollar sign, and ampersand. The lower case letters are arranged according to frequency of use, so they will be most readily available, and when purchased, supplied in larger quantities than the letters used less frequently. The upper case letters are arranged in alphabetical order with the exception of the J and U, which follow the Z.

should be assembled, and, previous to present-day casting methods, the nick was also useful in identifying the kind of type (2-2).

California Job Case

Most type used in hand composition is stored in California job cases. The California job case was made up to facilitate moving type in cases from the east to the west during the California gold rush.

Previous to the design of the Cali-

Spaces in California Job Case

The em quad is used for the inden-

2-3. California job case

ffi	fl	5 EM	4 EM	'	k		1	2	3	4	5	6	7	8		$			Æ	Œ	œ	œ
j	b	c	d		e		i		s		f	g	ff	9		A	B	C	D	E	F	G
?													fi	0								
!	l	m	n	h			o	y	p	w	,	EN QUADS	EM QUADS		H	I	K	L	M	N	O
z																						
x	v	u	t	3-EM SPACES			a	r	;	:		2-EM AND 3 M QUADS		P	Q	R	S	T	V	W
q										.	-				X	Y	Z	J	U	&	ffl

tion of paragraphs up to a measure of 18 picas. From 19 to 25 picas, the indention should be two ems; 26 to 35 picas, three ems, etc. The longer the measure, the greater the inden tion.

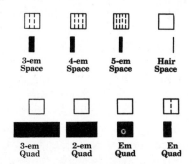

2-4. Spaces in California job case

The en quad is ½ the width of the em quad. It is the same width as modern figures. It is also considered the ideal space to use between words set in all upper case letters.

The 3-to-em space is ⅓ the width of the em quad and is frequently called a word space because it is considered the ideal space to use between words set in lower case letters.

The 4-to-em space is ¼ the width of the em quad, and the 5-to-em space is ⅕ the width of the em quad. They are frequently employed in spacing lines of type and justifying lines of type.

The two and three em quads are two and three times wider than the em quad. They are used for spacing out lines as well as for larger paragraph indentions.

Demon Characters

The beginner has trouble distinguishing between type characters which are similar in appearance. The characters in illustration 2-5 show how a piece of type looks, and directly below, how it will print.

After studying illustration 2-5, it will be noted that there are several letters such as d and q, p and b, n and u,

2-5. Demon characters

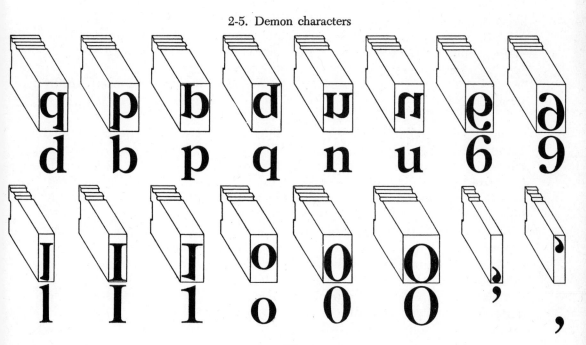

2-6. Removing type case from cabinet

and 6 and 9 which are opposites. For example, if the type character looks like a d, it will look like a q when it is printed, and vice versa.

Type must be read with the nicks "up" to insure accuracy.

Type Cabinets

Type cases are stored in cabinets. Cases should be handled with care because, if a case of type is dropped, the letters become mixed up—which is referred to as pied type. Considerable time will be required to sort the type and replace it into the type case.

In removing a type case from the cabinet (2-6), pull the case out about ten inches, get a firm hold of the case, then lift it onto the type bank, which is a slanted top work area especially designed for type composition and make-up (assembling type forms).

Composing Stick

The composing stick has four parts: the bed, knee, clamp, and half pica lever (2-7). The stick is graduated in picas and, by reversing the half pica lever, half pica measures may be obtained.

Leads and·Slugs

Metal strips of spacing material used between lines of type are referred to as two point leads and six point slugs. There are other point sizes available, but they are not commonly found in small shops. Leads and slugs are cut to pica lengths and are usually stored in type banks (2-8).

Composing Type

Since the composing stick is designed to be held in the left hand, for right-handed people, the beginning student who is left-handed may prefer to hold the composing stick in the right hand, which will leave the left hand free to pick up the type characters. To many left-handed students, this will seem more natural, although our best left-handed printers say they hold the stick right-handed style—in the left hand.

To set a line of type, insert a slug into the composing stick. The slug will measure the same length as the line to be set. Hold the composing stick in the left hand (2-9), pick up the type letters with the right hand, observing the position of the face and nick on the letter; as the letter is brought to the composing stick, rotate the letter so the nick will be to the open side of the stick and the face will be upward. The thumb of the left hand catches the letter as it is placed into the composing stick. The composing stick is held at an angle that would cause water to flow into

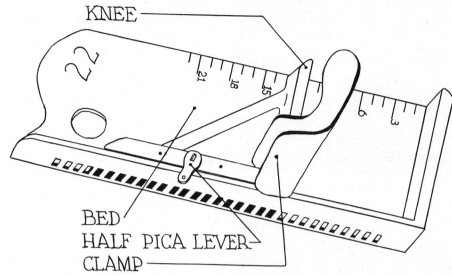

KNEE

BED
HALF PICA LEVER
CLAMP

2-7. Parts of composing stick

2-8. Typical lead and slug storage

2-9. Hold composing stick in left hand—
the right-handed way

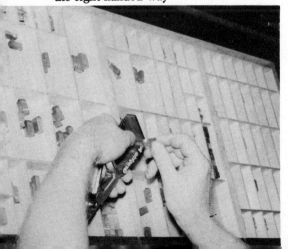

the corner formed by the knee and the bed. Make the left hand follow the right hand in picking up letters, to develop speed.

It is not difficult for the left-handed student to use the same method, so a left-hand style is not reviewed here.

When the line of type has been set, it must be spaced out so that it is snug in the composing stick. A simple test for snugness is to place a slug on top of the last line set, tip the stick forward slightly, and, if the line will support itself and not fall down, it is tight enough in the stick.

It is not recommended to fill the stick more than three quarters full of type, for the best handling. A stick half full of type should be maximum for the beginning student. Always place a slug in the stick after setting the last line of type.

Emptying Composing Stick

When type is to be removed from the composing stick, the stick is placed in a galley, which is a shallow,

15

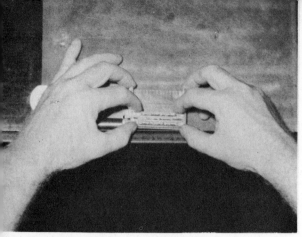

2-10. Place composing stick in galley

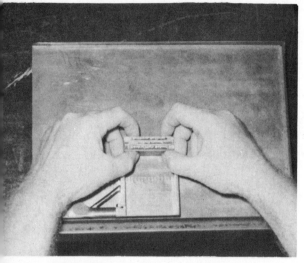

2-11. Slide type from composing stick

2-12. Move type to corner of galley

three-sided tray. The galley is on a slanted work bank, with the open end of the galley to the left of the compositor (2-10).

Place the thumbs on the first slug in the stick, the index fingers on the last slug, and the second fingers on the composing stick (2-10). Slide the type between the second fingers, which will "box in" the type (2-11). Move the type into the lower left corner of the galley so the nicks will be toward the open end of the galley (2-12).

Tying Up Type Form

When the type is safely in the galley, tie up the type form. This means to wrap string around it, so that the many parts will be held together tightly. Start the string in the exposed corner of type form (2-13), winding the string clockwise around the form several times, and then tucking in the end of the string under the windings in the open corner (2-14).

Proofing

Place the galley on the proof press with the cylinder to the left and the open end of the galley toward the cylinder (2-15). If the galley is placed at a slight angle, better proofs usually result because the cylinder of the proof press will first contact only a corner of the type form, and therefore is not as likely to slur the print.

With an ink knife, place a small quantity of proofing ink on the ink plate of the press (2-16). Distribute the ink with the brayer (a composition roller) (2-17). When the ink is evenly distributed, ink the type by rolling the brayer over the type with very light pressure (2-18).

Place a sheet of paper over the type form; then roll the cylinder over this

2-13. Tying up type form

2-14. **End of string tucked under windings**

2-15. Galley on bed of proof press

2-16. Place ink on plate

2-17. Distribute ink with brayer

2-18. Ink type form

2-19. Taking a proof

Proof Marks

At this point, read the proof carefully, checking against the original copy. There are standard symbols, called proof marks (2-20), which are used to indicate corrections. The symbols are placed in the margin of the proof either at the right or left of the error, and usually a path line is drawn from the specific spot of the correction.

Correcting Type Form

After errors have been marked on the proof, corrections in the type form are made. If a correction letter is to replace a letter of the same width, tweezers may be employed in making the change (2-21). Be careful not to damage the type by permitting the tweezers to slip off from the type body over the face of the letter. Be sure the type form is untied so the letter will pull easily. Type taken out of a form is always returned to the type case im-

assembly (2-19). Inspect the proof to see that it is clear and legible. If it is not, repeat this operation. The type must be perpendicular in the galley to take a good proof. Partially printed letters indicate the type is not standing up straight, which is referred to as type "off its feet." This can be corrected with the fingers by moving the lines or letters to a perpendicular position.

Moisten a wiping cloth with a solvent and wipe the excess ink from the type form; then remove the galley to a work bank.

2-20. Standard proof marks

Mark	Meaning	Mark	Meaning	Mark	Meaning
no ¶	No paragraph	✕	Defective letter	⊙	Colon
wf.	Wrong font letter	⊥	Push down space	;/	Semicolon
stet.	Let it stand	⹀	Turn over	⌄	Apostrophe
tr.	Transpose	ℬ	Take out	⌄"	Quotation
Caps.	Capitals	∧	Insert at this point	-/	Hyphen
S.C.	Small capitals	✓	Space evenly	///	Straighten lines
l.c.	Lower-case letter	✹	Insert space	⊏	Move over
ital.	Italic	⌣	Less space	□	Em quad space
Rom.	Roman letter	⊃⊂	Close up entirely	|¹|	One-em dash
(?)	Verify	⊙	Period	|²|	Two-em dash
O	Spell out	⁄	Comma	¶	Make paragraph

18

2-21. Removing a letter with tweezers

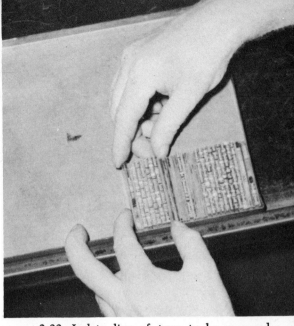

2-22. Isolate line of type to be removed from type form

mediately after the corrections have been made.

If the correction letter or letters to be inserted are not the same size as the letters to be taken out of the form, the line of type is returned to the composing stick before changing letters.

Separate the line to be removed from the form from the rest of the lines of type by several slugs on each side of the line to be removed (2-22).

Slide this line into the composing stick and make necessary adjustments so the length of the line will be exactly the same as the other lines of type in the form (2-23).

Return the corrected line to the galley in its proper position and remove the extra slugs from the type form by tipping up the slug on the exposed side of the form so you can easily get hold of it. (2-24).

After the desired space has been adjusted between lines of type, tie up the form, make a revised proof, and check again for errors.

2-23. Slide line into composing stick

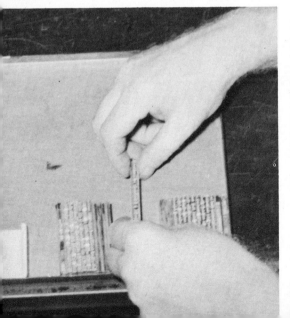

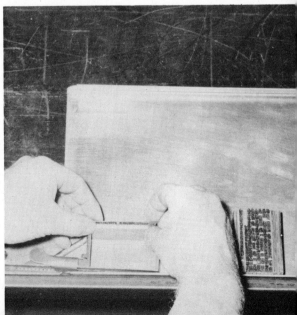

2-24. Removing extra space from type form

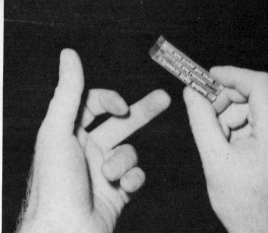

2-26. Hold lines of type in right hand

Distributing Type

When a type form has been printed, it is important that type be returned, or distributed, to the proper type case. Before distribution is started, compare the type in the line or lines with the type in the case. Although many types are similar, there are four check points to observe. They are: (1) size, (2) face, (3) width, and (4) nick. When these four items compare exactly with the type in the case, proceed with distribution.

Type to be distributed is placed in the lower corner of the galley with the nicks toward the open end. The bottom line of the type form is distributed first. If there are several lines to be distributed, the line or lines to be picked up are separated from the rest of the type form by several slugs that are the same length as the width or measure of the composition.

Place the thumb of each hand on the slug which separates the lines of type to be distributed from the lines remaining in the galley. The index finger is placed on the slug covering

2-27a. Right-handed person

2-25. Picking up lines of type for distribution

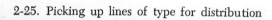

2-27b. Left-handed person

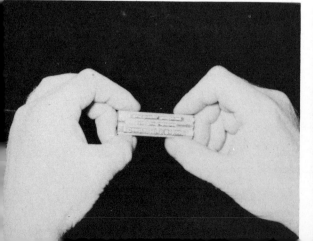

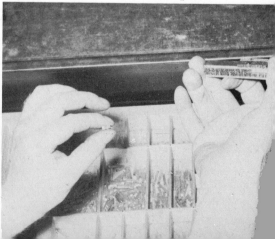

the last line. The second fingers cover the ends of the lines to be distributed (2-25).

Exert pressure on all four sides of the lines of type, which makes it possible to lift the lines of type without letters dropping out. When the lines have been lifted, elevate the left end, making it possible to hold the lines of type with the right hand (2-26).

Type transferred to the left hand (or possibly right hand for the left-handed student) is held in a horizontal position between the thumb and second finger, supported by the index finger under the lines of type (2-27a).

Start distributing type from the right side of the line (or left side of the line for left-handed students, 2-27b), picking up a word or a syllable at one time. Type to be distributed is held between the thumb and the index finger (2-28). Working the fingers back and forth will tend to separate the letters, which are then easily dropped into their proper compartment of the type case.

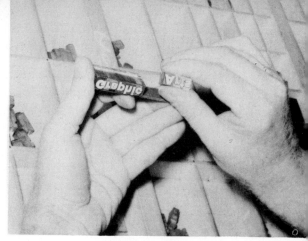

2-28. Distributing type

Word Spacing

The three-to-em space is considered the ideal space to use between words set in upper and lower case. When a line is justified, it is almost always necessary to increase or decrease space between words. Letters such as d, b, p, q, l, etc., are referred to as ascending and descending characters. When space must be increased between words, it is desirable to place additional space between one word ending and another word beginning with either ascending or descending

Paragraph Composition

This paragraph illustrates lines of type which have not been justified. The lines of type have been set flush to the left side of the composing stick which makes the margin on the left side neat and straight. The same amount of space was placed between all words and letters in the line. The margin on the right side is irregular, and it does not present a pleasing appearance.

2-29.

The lines of type in this paragraph were justified. Space between the words and letters has been adjusted so that each line is the same length. This was accomplished by increasing or decreasing the spaces placed between the words and letters. Both the margins on the left and right sides are neat and straight. Lines of type that have been justified please the eye.

2-30.

In paragraph composition for books, newspapers, and similar work, type is justified so it makes a full line (2-30), by increasing or decreasing space between words and letters of a line.

letters. It is also desirable to increase space between long words in preference to short words. Likewise short words can take reduced spaces better than longer words. Non-ascending or

-descending letters that end one word and begin the next word can take less space. Space following punctuation marks, particularly a comma, can be reduced with good effect.

Letterspacing

This line has not been letterspaced. T h i s   l i n e   h a s   b e e n   l e t - t e r s p a c e d .

2-31.

It is often necessary to add space *between letters of a word* to justify a line. When the space between *words* has been increased as much as two word spaces, and still the line has not been filled out, letterspacing is used. Place one thin space between each letter of the word or words. If two or more words are to be letterspaced, select words in different parts of the line.

Letterspacing is frequently employed in display composition just to achieve special effects.

Dividing Words

Words may be divided between syllables at the end of a line, provided the syllable contains two or more letters. It is better style to limit word divisions to not more than two successive lines, and it is preferred to have not more than one word division in three lines of type.

Borders

A border in typographic composition serves as a frame which might be compared to a picture frame. Borders should be selected to harmonize with the composition to be enclosed. A border might be a straight line, a combination of straight lines, or a design.

Borders composed of small pieces are referred to as piece border. Borders may also be made up of brass rule strips, or metal strips cast on Linotype, Elrod, or similar casting machines. Strip border may either be mitered or butted together at the corners, depending upon the design of the printing face.

When margins between the type and border have been established, first place space at the top and the bottom of the form. This spacing material measures the same as the composition; it might be either metal furniture, leads and slugs, or a combination of the three. If the border is to be butted, select proper length top and bottom pieces that will give the desired margin space on each side of the type form when the thickness of the border is deducted from the length of the top and bottom pieces of border. The side borders are within the top and bottom borders, and the length, of course, equals the length of the spacing material on each side of the type form. The same general procedure is used for placing piece border or mitered strip border around a form (2-32).

Combining Rule With Type

The term "rule" is used to describe material used to print lines. Rule is

2-32. Space arrangement between type and **border**

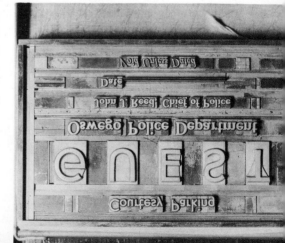

Date————————————————
　　　　Rule too high

Date————————————————
　　　　Rule too low

Date————————————————
　Rule too light, correct alignment

Date————————————————
Correct alignment, type and rule harmonize
2-33.

available to make lines ranging in weight from a hairline, which is a very fine line, to a solid twelve point line, which is very heavy. Rule is available in two point, six point, or 12 point *body* thickness. Lines to be written on should be of a weight that harmonizes with the type being used. Lightface type combines well with lightface rule. Heavier rule can be used with bolder type. Rules align with the bottom of type letters such as e, o, t, n, etc. (2-33).

When type and rule are composed in the same line, it is necessary to build up on each side of the rule (2-32). Since the body of the rule is almost always smaller than the type body, subtract the thickness of the rule body from the size of the type body. The remainder represents the amount of space that must be inserted in the line along with the rule. Whenever possible, use quads from a smaller size of type for spacing on top of the rule. Leads are frequently used in combination with the quads in order to make the rule align properly with the type (2-34).

Some Common Type Arrangements

There are several common type arrangements and indentions employed for pleasing effects where more than one line of type appears on a card or in similar composition.

2-34. Combining rule with type

CARL M. RAYSON
180 Washington Avenue
Dodge　　　　　　Iowa

　　　　　　　　block arrangement

CARL M. RAYSON
long, short, long　　180 Washington Avenue
　　　　　　Dodge ———————— Iowa

CARL M. RAYSON
180 Washington Avenue　　short, long, short
　　Dodge, Iowa

　　　　　　　　CARL M. RAYSON
flush right　　　　180 Washington Avenue
　　　　　　　　Dodge, Iowa

CARL M. RAYSON
180 Washington Avenue　　　flush left
Dodge, Iowa

This is a sample of a hanging indention in type
composition.

　　　　hanging indention

This is a sample of
a diagonal indention
in type composition.

　　　　diagonal indention

A half diamond arrange-
ment in type composition
is usually confined
to display
lines.

half diamond

Frequently it is possible to make
type arrangements conform to one of
the above examples. In printing personal stationery, when all three lines
are nearly the same length, it is desirable to vary the spacing between
words so that all lines will be the same
length when the type is set. Likewise
the short, long, short; the long, short,
long; or side aligning arrangements
allow for interesting variations.

Classification of Type Styles

Although there are hundreds of type
styles on the market, all of them can

be classified into seven groups according to their basic design. An un-
derstanding of each group will assist
the student to identify types and make
it easier to select appropriate type designs for a specific purpose.

Variation in the different parts of a
type face (2-35) provide a means for
classifying and identifying each style.

Oldstyle is a Roman type of letter
based on designs by Nicholas Jensen
in 1477. Some of the more common
identifying characteristics include the
small variation between thick and thin
strokes and the rounded serifs and fillets (2-36). Oldstyle types are still
very popular in many forms of typography. They may be composed in upper and lower case or all upper case
letters.

Modern, based on designs by Giam-
battista Bodoni in 1789, is also a Roman letter. Characteristic identifying
features include considerable contrast
between light and heavy strokes, a

2-35. Parts of printers type face

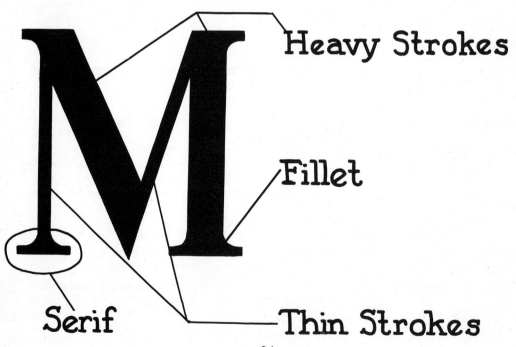

Garamond *and Italic*
Caslon 540 *and Italic*
2-36. Old style type faces

Bodoni *and Italic*
Bulmer Roman *and Italic*
2-37. Modern style type faces

Bernhard Gothic *and Italic*
Spartan *and Italic*
2-38. Sans serif type faces

geometrical, precise appearance, and fine serifs with no fillets (2-37). Modern type styles rival oldstyle designs in popularity in present-day advertising, book, and job printing. It is frequently composed in upper and lower case as well as all upper case letters. It lends itself to limited letter spacing, is quite legible, and is available from small to large sizes.

Sans serif was introduced into this country about a century ago, when it was mistakenly labeled "Gothic" by many type founders. "Sans" is a French preposition which means "without"—in other words, without serifs. Sans serif type did not become popular until 1927, when Paul Renner, of Germany, designed the Futura family. This type is characterized by not

having a serif, and little variation in the weight of letter design. Some sans serif type styles have no variation in the strokes of the letters (2-38).

Sans serif type is very popular in informal layouts and is extensively used in commercial printing and advertising, as well as for heads in books. It combines well with modern type designs, is well adapted to letter spacing, has fairly high legibility, and is available in both large and small sizes, bold, italic, condensed, and expanded.

Square serif styles became popular in 1931 when Heinrich Jost of Germany designed the Beton type family. The style is easily identified in that it resembles sans serif type with respect to stroke and the square serif is the same weight as the strokes of the let-

Stymie *and Italic*

2-39. Square serif type face

ters (2-39). It is a durable type, combines well with sans serif, and is available in small and large sizes and bold. It is still quite popular in commercial printing and advertising.

be avoided. Text type is not considered very legible in comparison with Roman letters; eight point is the smallest size commonly used. In the early 1900's it was widely used in commercial printing and advertising. However, at present it is generally restricted to ecclesiastical printing, Christmas greetings, and serious announcements.

Kaufmann Light Script

Bank Script

Grayda

Raleigh Cursive

2-40. Cursive style type faces

Cursive resembles handwriting and might include everything from a true script to types which are distinctively hand lettered (2-40). One of the first cursive type faces was cut by a typefounder in Holland in 1768. Most cursive types are not very legible in small sizes and are seldom available under 12 point. Two outstanding general rules should be observed in their use: namely, they should not be set in all upper case and they should be used sparingly in display composition. Letter spacing should be very limited and, in some cursive styles, should not be employed at all.

Text Type resembles the lettering of the scribes. Its original form precedes the design of the Roman letter (2-41). It should not be composed in all capitals and letter spacing should

SHADOW

Onyx

BALLOON HUXLEY

STENCIL

2-42. Occasional style type faces

Occasional styles are available in short fonts. They are distinctive types, extreme in design, and are frequently employed as "attention getters" in commercial advertising. Their use should be carefully planned, and the amount used should be restricted to retain their desirable qualities. Typical examples are shown in 2-42.

2-41. Text style type faces

Goudy Text

Engravers Old English

Cloister Text

American Text

Type faces may be further sub-divided into fonts, series, and families. A font of type is the smallest unit which consists of a complete assortment of type all of one body and face. Type founders package fonts of type in three parts: lower case, upper case, and figures. The quantity of each character in a font is based upon normal frequency of use. Typefounders specify the number of lower case and upper case A's contained in the font, the other letters, figures, and points being in proportion. Spaces and quads must be purchased in separate fonts.

A series of type refers to the various sizes in one design. For example, a series of Bodoni Bold would be a variety of sizes which would all be of the same design.

A family of type consists of two or more series of type which are variants of one basic design. A typical example would be the Bernhard Gothic family. Series of type are available in Bernhard Gothic light, Bernhard Gothic medium, and Bernhard Gothic heavy, to mention important members of the family.

Sample Tests—Chapter 2

Completion

Directions: Words or phrases have been omitted from the following statements. Fill in the proper word or phrase to make the statement complete and correct.

Example: 1. Movable type was invented by Johann Gutenberg in 1439.

1. Most type used in hand composition is stored in _____ _____ cases.
2. The lower case letters in a California job case are arranged according to_____
   _____ _____.
3. The upper case letters in a California job case are in alphabetical order with the exception of the letters _____ and _____ which follow the "Z".
4. The 3-to-em space is one third the width of the em quad and is frequently called a _____ space.
5. The two and three em quads are two and three times wider than the _____ quad.

Multiple Choice

Directions: Following each statement there are several answers, only one of which is correct. Place the letter preceding the correct answer in the space provided on the left of the question.

Example: b Color is imparted to printing ink by the (a) vehicle (b) pigment (c) drier.

_____ 6. In a block arrangement of three lines of type, (a) the middle line is shortest (b) the middle line is longest (c) the lines are all the same length.
_____ 7. Slugs are made of (a) wood (b) plastic (c) metal.
_____ 8. Cursive type (a) imitates hand writing (b) should be set in upper case letters (c) is available in six point.
_____ 9. Sans serif type (a) has a square serif (b) the serif has a fillet where it joins the stem (c) has no serif.
_____10. Square serif type styles resemble (a) Oldstyle type with a square serif (b) Modern type with a square serif (c) Sans serif type with a square serif.

Matching

Directions: The words or phrases in the column on the right match one of the words or phrases in the column on the left. Place the letter preceding the matching word or phrase of the column on the right in the blank space provided in the column on the left.

Example: _a_ 1. Form   a. Type

_____11. Type   a. Proof press

_____12. String   b. Oldstyle

_____13. Brayer   c. Nick

_____14. Caslon   d. Variations of a basic type design

_____15. Family   e. Tying up type form

True-False

Directions: The following statements are either true or false. If the statement is true, circle the "T" at the left of the numbered item. If the statement is false, circle the "F".

Example: Ⓣ F 1. Leads available in most small shops are two points thick.

T F 16. In the long, short, long arrangement of three lines of type, the middle line is shorter than the top and bottom line.

T F 17. When using strip border, the side borders should overlap the top and bottom borders.

T F 18. A series of type contains several sizes of type which have the same design.

T F 19. It is not considered advisable to set text type in all capital letters.

T F 20. The printing term "rule" refers to a measuring device.

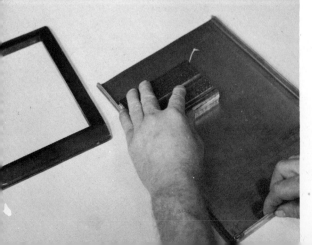

3-1. Slide form onto imposing surface

3-2. Place chase over type form

Chapter 3

ALMOST EVERY general commercial printing plant is equipped with a hand-fed platen press for printing the smaller short run forms. It is a clamshell type of press, simple to operate, yet it can be very dangerous to the uninstructed operator.

Locking Up Form

There are two common methods employed to lock forms in a platen press chase. (A chase is a metal rectangular frame which holds the type on the bed of the press.)

The type form is slid from the galley onto the imposing surface (3-1), which is a smooth metal or stone top table.

The heading of the type form should be to the left, or to the bottom, of the chase, depending upon the shape of the form (3-2). Usually the form is located so the long way of the paper to be printed will conform to the long way of the chase. Whenever possible, it is desirable to locate the form so the paper can be positioned to approximately the center of the chase.

Measure the width and length of the type form (3-3), selecting two pieces of wood furniture that are slightly longer than each measurement. Wood furniture is the larger pieces of spacing material, made of wood.

Wood furniture is placed around the type form, overlapping one piece over the next piece (3-4). This is called by some printers the "chaser" method of lockup. String may now be removed from around the type form.

Quoins are then placed to the top and to the right of the form (3-5). Quoins are expanded with a key to lock the type form in the chase. Fill space to left and bottom of the type form with furniture.

Wood furniture is used to fill in the remaining space inside the chase (3-6). Be careful that one piece of furniture does not bind another piece. If the type form is small, pyramid the

3-3. Measure width and length of type form

3-4. Wood furniture around the form

3-5. **Position quoins** to top and right

3-6. Quoins and furniture in position

3-7. Tighten quoins lightly

3-8. Plane type form

furniture to the edge of the chase so that pressure will be distributed over a wider area. Reglets (wood spacing material 6 points or 12 points thick) are used to fill spaces which are too small for wood furniture.

Quoins are tightened very lightly (3-7). A "planer" (block of wood) and mallet are then used to level the type so that all printing surfaces are even. This is referred to as planing a type form (3-8).

Tighten each quoin a small amount and repeat two or three times until the form is tight in the chase. For small chases and forms, adequate tightness will be obtained by exerting pressure on the quoin key with just the thumb and first finger of the right hand.

Raise the chase slightly, then tap the face of the type with the fingers. If the type does not move, it is safe to lift the form from the imposing surface and place it in the press (3-9). In making this test, do not

30

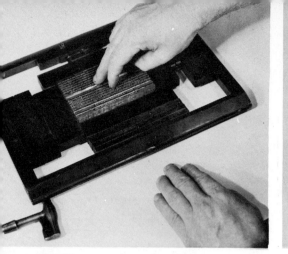

3-9. Test type form for "lift"

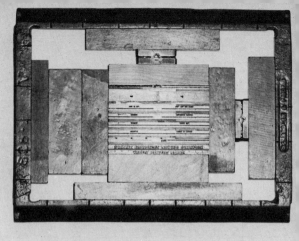

3-10. Furniture-within-furniture lockup

raise the form over ½ inch from the imposing surface, so if the letters are not tight they will not fall out of the type form. Quoins may then be loosened and the loose lines re-justified. A form that can be raised without pieces dropping out is said to "lift."

The furniture - within - furniture method of lockup can be employed when the width of the type form is in multiples of five. Two pieces of furniture must be the same length as the width of the type form so that they may be enclosed by furniture on the two sides (3-10). This method should be used for small type forms whenever possible because the lockup will be more rigid. The only difference between the two methods is the arrangement of the four pieces of furniture next to the type form.

Preparation of Press

Platen presses require daily oiling. Turn the press so the rollers rest on

3-11. Parts of platen press

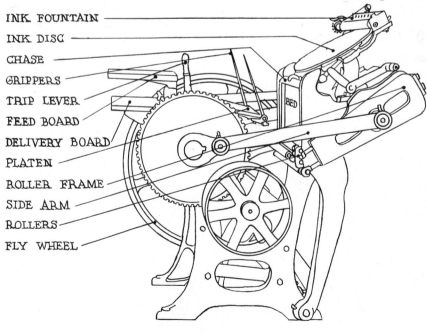

INK FOUNTAIN
INK DISC
CHASE
GRIPPERS
TRIP LEVER
FEED BOARD
DELIVERY BOARD
PLATEN
ROLLER FRAME
SIDE ARM
ROLLERS
FLY WHEEL

BED

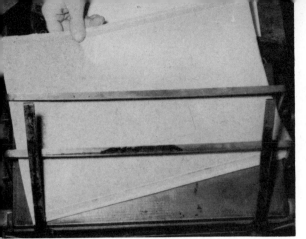

3-12. Remove drawsheet from press

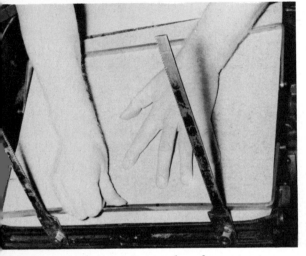

3-13. Attach new drawsheet

the ink disk. Begin oiling all bearings in front of the delivery board and work around the press clockwise, oiling every bearing.

For every different job to be

printed, it is necessary to "dress" the platen (3-11). This means to replace the packing and the drawsheet, which has been stretched tightly across the surface of the platen. A special paper is used for this purpose. It is an oily, tough paper of uniform thickness which is called tympan paper.

The drawsheet is held in place by two bales, one at the top and the other at the bottom of the platen. The bales must be raised to release the tympan paper (3-12).

The new drawsheet is cut to fit the platen, large enough to extend ⅝ inch beyond the platen on the bale sides (3-13).

Fasten the drawsheet with the lower bale first, spread both hands over the drawsheet pressing downward and pulling the hands to the top of the platen. The top bale is closed by the heel of the hand (3-14).

The amount of initial packing used will depend upon how the platen on the press has been adjusted. Check with your instructor. A minimum of three sheets of 60 pound book paper is recommended for the smallest forms (3-15). (For discussion of paper weight, see Chaper 5). The beginner should always start with the minimum amount of packing for which the press has been previously adjusted.

3-14. Stretch drawsheet over platen

3-15. Insert initial packing

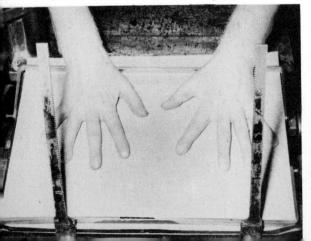

Press Makeready

A small quantity of ink is placed on the ink disk with a spatula (3-16). The press is started on slow speed and run until the ink is evenly distributed on the disk. Stop the press when the rollers are at their lowest point of travel. In this position the platen is open and the bed is fully exposed.

The locked type form is then transferred to the press with the quoins up and to the right (3-17). The bottom of the chase is rested upon two lugs at the bottom of the bed, the clamp at the top of the bed raised, the form pushed back to the bed, and the chase clamp allowed to snap down on the chase (3-18).

Position of the form in relation to the grippers must be checked at this point (3-19). Standing by the feed board, sight along the form and, if the grippers do not clear the type form, move them by loosening the binding screw; slide gripper on gripper bar; then tighten the screw.

Double check to see that the grippers clear the type form. The press may now be started and, after turning over several times, the trip lever is pulled toward the operator. This places the press on impression, and a print is made on the drawsheet (3-20). Push the trip lever forward to take the press "off" impression.

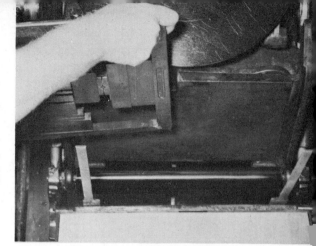

3-17. Lift chase into press

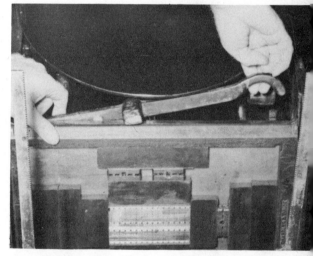

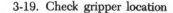

3-18. Allow clamp to snap down on chase

Stop the press and examine the print made on the drawsheet. If no print is made, it indicates that there is not sufficient packing under the drawsheet. Add another sheet of book paper; then repeat, taking another im-

3-16. Inking the press

3-19. Check gripper location

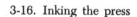

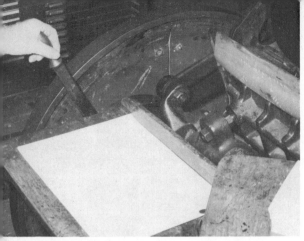

3-20. Make first impression on drawsheet

the drawsheet and packing. This may injure the type as well as destroy the smooth surface of the drawsheet and packing, which is necessary to get a good clear, sharp print on paper.

When a print on the drawsheet has been made which is clear enough to show the outline of the type form, the paper position can be determined. *Do not increase the amount of packing* to make a clear print on the drawsheet. Lay a piece of paper stock to be printed over the impression on the drawsheet to mark the position of the side guide. When possible, line up the top of the paper with a printed portion of the form to aid in making

pression. It is important not to add more than one sheet at a time in order to make a light impression. If too much packing is used, it will result in a heavy impression which will emboss

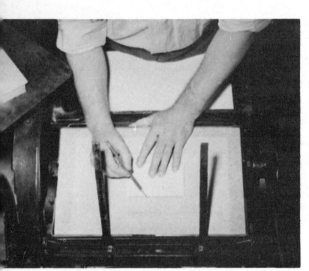

3-21. Scribe line for side guide

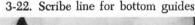

3-22. Scribe line for bottom guides

3-23. Space guides for easy feeding

3-24. Attach gauge pins to drawsheet

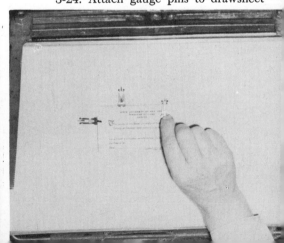

an accurate estimate of paper location. Using the paper as a square, scribe a line on the drawsheet (3-21).

Move the sheet of paper to give the desired margin at the top. Scribe a line, using the piece of paper to be printed as a square. This will mark the approximate position of the sheet on the drawsheet (3-22).

Place the piece of paper on the lines scribed on the drawsheet to mark the position of the guides. Guides used on a platen press are called gauge pins (3-23). Two gauge pins are used for the bottom and should be located approximately ¼ the length of the sheet in from each side. The position of the side guide should be approximately ¼ the distance upward from the bottom of the sheet. Place an "x" at these spots to indicate gauge pin location.

Start the point of the gauge pin ¼ inch below the line at the point marked with an "x" (3-24). Push the pin down about ½ inch; then hold the thumb on the drawsheet to bring the point through it. Slide the pin down to the line.

The tongue of the gauge pin now is checked to make sure it will not touch the type when an impression is made.

With a solvent on a wiping cloth, clean the excess ink from the drawsheet to prevent offsetting the impres-sion to the back of the sheet of paper to be printed (3-25).

On the platen, place a sheet of paper to be printed, which will be positioned by the guides (3-26). Start the press, taking an impression on the paper. When a print has been made, check (1) location on sheet, (2) amount of impression, (3) amount of ink, (4) typographical errors and damaged type.

Gauge pins may be adjusted so the printing will be in the desired location; keep in mind that the paper is moved—the type form is stationary (3-27).

Sufficient impression is made to print the form clearly. It may be necessary to add packing to the press; however, only one sheet is added before another impression is made. If the type is close to printing clearly, often only a sheet of tissue paper should be added—in no case no more than one sheet of book paper.

The correct amount of ink is difficult for the beginner to judge. A simple test is to lay a sheet of paper on the delivery board and, with a clean finger, smear the resultant print. If little or no smudge results, add a small amount of ink (about the size of a pea). Start the press to distribute this ink, before taking another impression. If the ink smudges very easily and to a considerable degree,

3-25. Clean impression from drawsheet

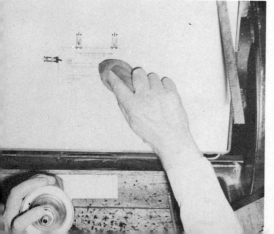

3-26. Position paper at guides

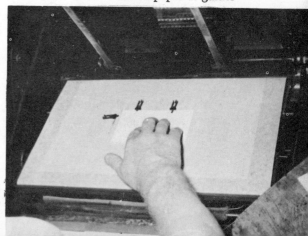

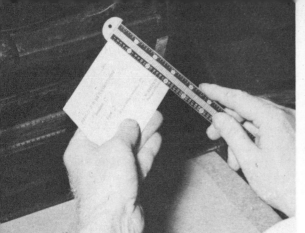

3-27. Check location of printing

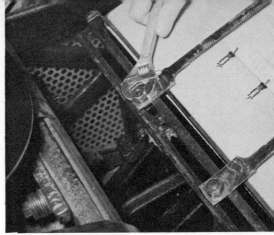

3-28. Move grippers to margin

it indicates too much ink on the press.

If typographical errors or damaged type occur, the chase is removed from the press, then placed on the imposing surface, where necessary corrections can be made.

Another sheet may now be printed. Check carefully the same four points described on page 35, correcting the items as required. This procedure is repeated until the print is satisfactory.

Keep in mind that no more impression should be used than necessary to make a clear print, and only enough ink should be applied to make the form print clearly. (A small form will require less ink and less impression than a large form.)

Some kinds of paper will have a tendency to stick to the type form, and, when the platen opens, the sheet will not remain in place. Grippers are designed to hold the sheet to the platen. They may be moved to the margin on the left and right side of the sheet being printed (3-28). However, in no case should the gripper be placed in a position to interfere with the type form when an impression is made.

When side margins are not sufficient to locate the grippers, a string or strings may be stretched between the grippers to catch the upper or lower margin (3-29). Depress the grippers to check the location of the string with the impression on the drawsheet. Type or rule permitted to print on string will be damaged and will have to be discarded. Check this carefully.

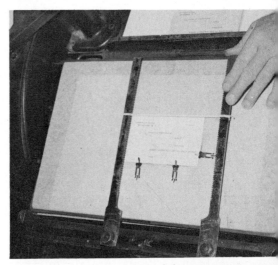

3-29. String stretched between grippers

3-30. Tap pins down

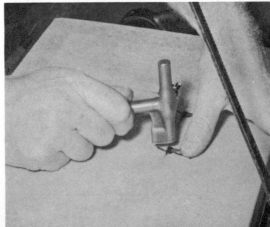

36

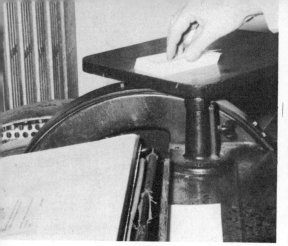

3-31. Pick up sheet with right hand

3-32. Place sheet on platen

Double check location of the printing on the sheet. If the location is correct, and the printing is square on the sheet, the gauge pins are tapped down (3-30). The two small points of the gauge pin which are imbedded in the drawsheet prevent the pin from slipping. When card stock is being printed, it is advisable to also seal the pins. A drop of ordinary melted sealing wax is sufficient to seal the pin to the drawsheet.

The counter now is set, a small quantity of paper to be printed placed on the feed board, and all other materials or tools removed from the press.

Press Feeding

Start the press on slow speed; pick up a sheet of paper with right hand, thumb under the sheet and four fingers fanned out on top of the sheet (3-31). The sheet to be fed is held in the right hand and, as the platen opens, it is placed on the platen.

When the sheet contacts the platen, remove the thumb from the back of the sheet and, with finger tips, slide the sheet to the bottom guides; then slide to the side guide (3-32).

As the platen begins to close, the hand is withdrawn from the press even if the positioning of the sheet has not been completed. The position-

ing operation may be completed the next time the platen opens. Use only the right hand to position the sheet. When the sheet has been positioned, place the press on impression, and, when printed, withdraw the sheet by sliding it from the platen with the fingers of the left hand. In the event the finger used to slide the printed sheet from the platen must contact the printed area, use a sandpaper finger stole on the finger used to withdraw the sheet (3-33). When the sheet has been taken from the platen, take the press off impression by pushing forward on the trip lever.

Safety Precautions

As a beginner, you should attempt to print only one sheet in five or six revolutions of the press until you are familiar with the action of the press and able readily to pick up sheets to be fed into the press.

3-33. Feeding platen press

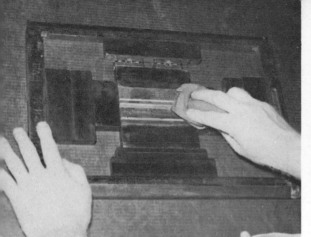

3-34. Clean type form

3-35. Wash ink disk

Under no condition place your hands anywhere except on the feedboard, above the gauge pins on the platen, and on the delivery board, when the press is in operation. Always stop the press when a sheet of paper must be removed from any other position. Stand erect at the delivery board; never lean over the platen to position a sheet. Tremendous pressure is exerted between the bed of the press and the platen, and the exercise of extreme care in operation cannot be overemphasized, to prevent an accident.

If you are not sure of your actions, are afraid of operating the press, or have some serious physical impairment, don't operate a power driven platen press.

At first, stop the press when adding ink to the ink disk. Place the ink on the left side of the ink disk, then idle the press until it is completely distributed.

When the right hand has positioned a sheet on the platen, it immediately returns to the feed board to pick up another sheet, which is in the hand ready to be fed as the platen opens. If the sheet is not ready, skip one printing cycle to make sure ample time will be available to feed and position the sheet. Take no chances.

Press feeding requires practice to attain speed. However, speed is not important to the beginner. Take your time, think about what you are doing, feed the paper accurately, and speed and skill will develop with practice.

Cleaning the Platen Press

After the presss run has been completed, place the chase on the imposing surface. With cleaning solvent, moisten a wiping cloth to clean the type form (3-34).

Clean the press by washing the ink disk (3-35); then roll the press over by hand until the rollers are near the disk.

Wash the rollers as the press is turned slowly by hand, which will raise the cleaned rollers onto the clean ink disk (3-36). Make sure that the ends, as well as the middle of the rollers, are cleaned.

The ink spatula is cleaned, and the ink cans covered and returned to storage. Unlock the type form and tie up with string in the usual manner. Slide the tied form into the galley and return to the work bank for distribution.

Hand Lever Presses

The principles of operating the hand lever press (3-37) are the same as for a power platen press except

3-36. Wash press rollers

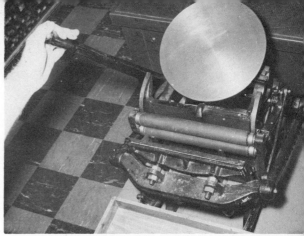

3-37. Hand lever press

that the platen is closed with hand lever action, and the presses are smaller and are designed for printing small forms of short runs. Only one person should operate the press. In no case should one do the press feeding and another operate the lever.

Printing Inks

Ink used in graphic arts is made up of pigment, vehicle, and drier. Ink manufacturers have their own formulas and make different kinds of ink for many different printing surfaces.

Ink is colored by pigment which is obtained from various sources in the mineral, vegetable, and animal kingdoms.

The vehicle provides the body of the ink and serves as a binder which holds the color to the paper. Varnish, linseed oil, or rosin is used for the vehicle.

Driers such as cobalt or magnesium may be added to the ink to act as a catalyst in drying.

Different colors of ink are derived by mixing the three primary colors of red, blue, and yellow, plus black and white. When mixing ink, a color wheel is recommended for a guide in selecting inks to be mixed. Add dark to light only in small amounts.

For the inexperienced, it is recommended that a reliable ink manufac-turer be depended upon to supply the proper ink for the kind of paper or other material to be printed.

In the graphic arts laboratory, bond ink, job ink, book ink, and news ink are usually kept in stock for letterpress printing. Lithograph inks should be stocked for the different materials to be printed by this process. A general purpose silk screen ink, and perhaps textile ink, should be kept available for silk screen printing. The primary colors, plus black and white, are usually kept in stock for each printing process.

When special problems arise, such as an unusual surface is to be printed or an exact color match is required, it is recommended that a reliable ink manufacturer be consulted.

Most printers ink for school use is purchased in one pound cans. Silk screen ink is available in pint and quart cans. When a new can of ink is opened, cover the label with transparent tape to keep the label clean. Grease the inside lip of the cover to make it easy to remove as well as to make the can more air tight. Ink is removed from the can with an ink knife. *Do not dig holes in the ink.* When the surface of the ink becomes covered with "skin", be sure to remove all of the skin before using ink from the can.

Completion

Directions: Words or phrases have been omitted from the following statements. Fill in the proper word or phrase to make the statement complete and correct.

Example: Movable type was invented by *Johann Gutenberg* in 1439.

1. A chase is a metal _____ frame which holds the type on the bed of the press.
2. Tympan paper is a special paper designed for _____ _____ on presses.

3. In making ready on a platen press, it is necessary to _____ the platen for every job.
4. A type form locked in a chase is said to _____ when all pieces in the form are tight.
5. When making ready on a platen press, there are four points to check on the printed sheet. They are (a)_____
   (b) _____ (c) _____
   (d) _____.

Multiple Choice

Directions: Following each statement there are several answers, only one of which is correct. Place the letter preceding the correct answer in the space provided on the left of the question.

Example: <u>b</u>   1. Color is imparted to printing ink by the (a) vehicle (b) pigment (c) drier.

_____ 6. The heading of the type form is usually placed in the chase (a) to the top or left (b) to bottom or right (c) bottom or left.

_____ 7. Grippers on a platen press must clear the type form. This should be checked (a) right after the chase has been placed on the press (b) before the chase is placed on the press (c) after the first impression has been made on the drawsheet.

_____ 8. It is considered safe practice in feeding a platen press to (a) pick up a sheet of paper from the floor under the press while it is running (b) only place hands on the feed board, on the delivery table, and on the platen above the gauge pins (c) retrieve a misfed sheet of paper.

_____ 9. An imposing surface is (a) any flat smooth surface (b) a smooth metal or stone top table (c) a smooth top table made of hard maple.

_____10. The three primary colors are (a) yellow, blue, green (b) green, yellow, red (c) yellow, red, blue.

Matching

Directions: The words or phrases in the column on the right match one of the words or phrases in the column on the left. Place the letter preceding the matching work or phrase of the column on the right in the blank space provided in the column on the left.

Example:

   <u>a</u>   1. Drawsheet   a. Tympan paper

_____11. Lockup   a. Level type
_____12. Chase   b. Stand erect to feed the platen press

_____13. Safe practice   c. Quoin
_____14. Unsafe   d. Oil press while running

_____15. Planer   e. Rectangular frame

True-False

Directions: The following statements are either true or false. If the statement is true, circle the "T" at the left of the numbered item. If the statement is false, circle the "F".

Example: T Ⓕ 1. Two persons always work at the press at one time.

T F 16. Type should be lifted from the galley and placed in about the center of the chase in preparation for locking up the type form.

T F 17. The furniture-within-furniture method of lockup may be used when the width of the type form is in multiples of five.

T F 18. The platen press should be inked after the chase has been placed in the press.

T F 19. The point of the gauge pin should be started on the line scribed on the drawsheet, which indicates the outer margin.

T F 20. It is necessary to oil a platen press every day it is being used.

Chapter 4

A LAYOUT is a plan for the typographer (typesetter) to follow. It may be compared to a blueprint used by a carpenter in building a house. Since the layout is a plan, it is important that it be ready before work is started in order to proceed in an intelligent manner.

Graphic arts activities provide excellent media for creative expression, which in turn gives the student an opportunity to make an application of the principles of art. Therefore a good layout should not only be a specific plan for the typographer, but it should also embody the principles of good design. These are balance, emphasis, continuity, and contrast.

In a well balanced layout, equal weight will appear on each side of a vertical line through the center of the layout. In *formal layouts,* where all lines of type and illustrations are centered, balance is automatic. *Informal layouts* call for flush left and flush right as well as other arrangements in type, ornaments, and illustrations. In this case, the center of the page can be compared to a fulcrum; for example, a large area of type near the fulcrum can be balanced by a smaller area of type further from the fulcrum.

Emphasis in a layout refers to the relative dominance of the parts. The most dominant part of the layout will be that of greatest importance.

A layout should have *continuity,* which is a harmonious relationship of the various parts.

Contrast refers to making the parts of a layout different to relieve monotony and stimulate reader interest. This may be achieved by a variation in spacing, by a variation in type sizes, by a variation in type styles, or by a variation in color.

In planning the elements of a design which include line, form, color, texture, and space, it is essential that the basic principles of design be applied.

All layouts are started with copy which has been written. The copy should be checked for correct spelling, correct punctuation, and correct grammatical expression.

The designer should clearly understand the function of the printed piece. Form should grow out of function and use. How it is to be used, where it is to be used, and when it is to be used might all have a bearing on the design. For example, color scheme, type selection, and illustrations appropriate for a Christmas program would not be appropriate for a Fourth of July program.

The size, kind, color, and weight of stock should be determined. Some forms of printing, such as wedding announcements, stationery, informal cards, tickets, and envelopes, are just a few examples that use stock available only in standard sizes. Consult a paper supply sample catalog to decide upon a specific stock for the printed piece.

Many good designs and excellent layouts fail because they are not suited to the equipment at hand. For example, the area of a linoleum block to be printed on a platen press should not exceed one half of the area of the press. When the capacity of the press is exceeded, the inking mechanism is inadequate, and the impression is not strong enough to make good prints. Also, we must use the most suitable method or process. It is not practical to reproduce a photograph by letterpress if the paper stock is too rough; however, the offset method may be used. Likewise, bright, reflective signs are successfully reproduced by silk screen because a heavy deposit of ink is laid down, but the same signs printed by the relief process (letterpress) are inferior because only a thin deposit of ink is laid on the sheet.

Typographical treatment may be affected by current styles, tradition, and even state or federal laws. Type styles, like styles of architecture and clothing, change. Early in 1900, text type ("Old English") was widely used in many forms of printing, from letterheads to business announcements. Currently, text type is almost exclusively limited to ecclesiastical and other very formal printing. Announcements and other forms of social printing are set in certain formal type styles, whereas advertising displays, television play titles, and other attention-getting layouts demand special styles. State and Federal laws govern typographical treatment to some degree in the printing of ballots, labels, envelopes, legal forms, and political advertising.

There are two steps in layout: (1) the rough layout, and (2) the working or finished layout. The rough layout is used to "crystalize" a mental image into size, shape, and form. From the rough layout, the working or finished layout is evolved. All working layouts for graphic arts should be actual size, made on the color of paper to be used and with the final color of ink. Styles of type, their size and location, should be indicated clearly on the layout, in order to make it possible to visualize how the job will look after it has been completed.

Rough layouts can be made on a small scale in proportion to the finished size so that the organization of the copy can be quickly and easily visualized. These are merely sketches to express an idea. Many roughs may be made before a layout that fits the purpose has been evolved. The selected rough layout then is used as a guide in making the finished layout.

Very small sizes of type, which are difficult to letter by hand, are frequently indicated by rectangular shaded areas the same size as the type and in a tone that is comparable to the type to be used. Bold type is indicated by a dark shaded area; light type is indicated by a lighter shaded area. Copy for these areas is usually typed separately, using the layout as a guide for position and measure.

Finished layouts are done on paper which is larger than the finished piece in order to provide space to indicate size and kind of type, etc., in the margin. Lines of type not actually lettered in the layout can be typewritten below, and keyed to their location. Typewritten copy usually is placed on a separate sheet, together with other details on illustrations, and kind, weight, and color of stock, so that artists and typesetters can have copy of

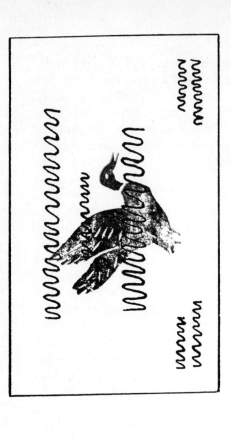

4-1. Rough layouts

44

18 PT BRUSH

8 PT BODONI

12 PT BODONI

4-2. Finished layout

their own and the layout will not become soiled or damaged with too much handling. The typewritten copy might be as follows:

Ticket #2098—Bennett Jr. Hi. printshop—ready date April 24

    (copy) Annual Spring Dinner
    (line block) Sunday Mar 24
                Jefferson Hotel
                Admission $1.00
                Serving 1-3 pm
    Jeff Rod and Gun Club

On the copy, as well as on the layout, letter or write the type styles and sizes, and dimensions of the type areas. The drawing or linoleum block of the goose also is separate. (For printing, a linoleum block is mounted on wood, type high. This can best be demonstrated by your instructor.)

Type specimen sheets containing upper case and lower case alphabets must be used as a guide to make accurate layouts (4-4). Most shops print specimen sheets of all styles and sizes of type available in their type library. In the ab-sence of type specimen sheets, type catalogs, supplied by typefounders, may be used, if these types are available to you in your shop.

Use type specimen sheets to select type styles and sizes which will fit the layout. To determine length of line, count the number of letters and spaces in a given line of the copy; then count off a like number of characters on the type specimen sheet. These sheets may also be used to match sizes and styles of type shown roughly on the finished layout.

No matter how simple the job may be, a working layout is indispensable for the beginner. Make your own layouts, beginning with the very simple and gradually advancing to more complex printed pieces.

4-3. Printed copy

45

Janson

Since effective communication requires both the conception and the practice of methods and procedures of science, craft, and art, the essential parts of composition have been treated .in this text from this threefold point of view. Principles, involving verified facts, laws, proximate causes, and exact observation, are explained; cleverness, ingenuity, and finish are given consideration; and the employment of particular means in order to produce certain definite results,

ABCDEFGHIJKLMNOPQRSTUVWXYZ   1234567890   ABCDEFGHIJKLMNOPQRSTUVWXYZ

Width in Picas	1	10	12	14	16	18	20	22	24	26	28	30
Characters	3	30	36	42	48	54	60	66	72	78	84	90

Since effective communication requires both the conception and the practice of methods and procedures of science, craft, and art, the essential parts of composition have been treated in this text from this threefold point of view. Principles, involving verified facts, laws, proximate causes, and exact observation, are explained; cleverness, ingenuity, and finish are given consideration; and the

ABCDEFGHIJKLMNOPQRSTU   1234567890   ABCDEFGHIJKLMNOPQRSTU

Width in Picas	1	10	12	14	16	18	20	22	24	26	28	30
Characters	2.55	26	31	36	41	46	51	56	61	66	71	77

Since effective communication requires both the conception and the practice of methods and procedures of science, craft, and art, the essential parts of composition have been treated in this text from this threefold point of view. Principles, involving verified facts, laws, proximate causes, and exact observation, are explained; cleverness, ingenuity, and finish are given considera-

ABCDEFGHIJKLMNOPQRS   1234567890   ABCDEFGHIJKLMNOPQRS

Width in Picas	1	10	12	14	16	18	20	22	24	26	28	30
Characters	2.45	25	29	34	39	44	49	54	59	64	69	74

Since effective communication requires both the conception and the practice of methods and procedures of science, craft, and art, the essential parts of composition have been treated in this text from this threefold point of view. Principles, involving verified facts, laws, proximate causes, and exact observation, are explained; cleverness, ingenuity, and finish are

ABCDEFGHIJKLMNOPQRSTUVWXYZ   1234567890   ABCDEFG

Width in Picas	1	10	12	14	16	18	20	22	24	26	28	30
Characters	2 3	23	28	32	37	41	46	51	55	60	64	69

4-4a.

Garamond Bold

14 PT. GARAMOND BOLD—HAND
WARM SUNLIGHT IS THE GIFT OF NATURE   2345
New type faces in the modern mode are essential to meet the p

18 PT. GARAMOND BOLD—HAND
WARM SUNLIGHT IS THE GIFT OF 2345
New type faces in the modern mode are essenti

24 PT. GARAMOND BOLD—HAND
WARM SUNLIGHT IS TH   2345
New type faces in the modern mode

30 PT. GARAMOND BOLD—HAND
WARM SUNLIGHT IS 234
New type faces in the modern

36 PT. GARAMOND BOLD—HAND
WARM SUNLIGH 234
New type faces in the m

42 PT. GARAMOND BOLD—HAND
WARM SUNLI 234
New type faces in the

48 PT. GARAMOND BOLD—HAND
WARM SUN 234
New type faces in t

4-4b.

Sample Tests—Chapter 4

Completion

Directions: Words or phrases have been omitted from the following statements. Fill in the proper word or phrase to make the statement complete and correct.

Example: A layout is a *plan* for the typographer to follow.

1. The principles of design which should be applied to all layouts are _____

   _____ _____ _____ .

2. Form grows out of _____ .
3. The area of a linoleum block to be printed on a platen press should not exceed _____ _____ the area of the press.
4. Successful reproduction of a photograph on rough stock is practical when the _____ method of reproduction is used.
5. Display type is generally used in _____ printing.

Multiple Choice

Directions: Following each statement there are several answers, only one of which is correct. Place the letter preceding the correct answer in the space provided on the left of the question.

Example: a   1. A working or finished typographic layout should be (a) actual size (b) smaller than actual size (c) larger than actual size (d) about actual size.

_____ 6. The rough layout may differ from a finished layout in (a) general form (b) size (c) shape.

_____ 7. The layout (a) should be changed by the typographer as work progresses (b) should be made after the type is composed (c) should be completed before composition is started.

_____ 8. Equipment for production of a job (a) should be considered before making the layout (b) is unimportant (c) is important but should not limit the designer.

_____ 9. The designer must give consideration to many factors in planning a job. Select one of the following which is of least importance: (a) equipment for production (b) selection of suitable printing process (c) using standard color or colors of ink.

_____10. The designer should clearly understand the function or use of a printed piece because (a) the customer is always right (b) the copy should be correct (c) it has a bearing on the design.

Matching

Directions: The words or phrases in the column on the right match one of the words or phrases in the column on the left. Place the letter preceding the true matching word or phrase, column on the right, in the blank space provided in the column on the left.

Example: a   1. Measure   a. Ruler

_____11. Layout   a. Small type sizes

_____12. Social   b. Samples of printing type

_____13. Rectangular   c. Books on shaded etiquette areas

_____14. Silk screen   d. Blueprint

_____15. Type   e. Reflective sheet signs

True-False

Directions: The following statements are either true or false. If the statement is true, circle the "T" at the left of the numbered item. If the statement is false, circle the "F".

Example: Ⓣ F 1. The area of a linoleum block should not exceed over half the area of the platen press on which it is to be printed.

T F 16. Typographical treatment on some jobs may be affected by state or federal laws.

T F 17. Prepared copy is the starting point for making a layout.

T F 18. Photographs can be successfully printed by letterpress on rough stock.

T F 19. Making several rough layouts precedes the finished layout.

T F 20. Type specimen sheets are not essential in making finished layouts.

Chapter 5

SEVERAL operations and machines *serve,* but are not a part of, one or more areas of graphic arts. Since their relative importance or complexity does not seem to warrant separate chapters for each one, they have been grouped together here.

Slug Cutter

Spacing material used between lines of type is available in "labor-saving" fonts. A labor-saving font is an assortment of leads and slugs which have been cut to lengths commonly needed in hand composition.

This material is also sold in longer lengths so the printer can cut it to size in his own shop. For this he uses a slug cutter, although the trimmer saw can be used instead. (See the following page.) The lead and slug cutter is adjustable to pica and half-pica measures (5-1).

Mitering Machine

Corners on borders around printed forms are frequently neater if the corners are mitered rather than butted together.

The mitering machine illustrated here is designed to miter corners on

5-2. Mitering machine

soft metal rule and border material (5-2). It is adjustable to various angles, which makes precision possible. More elaborate machines are also available which are power operated and designed to cut two angles at one time.

Trimmer Saw

The trimmer saw is a precision machine designed to cut metal spacing materials and plates. To a large degree, it replaces the slug cutter.

The material holder is graduated in

5-1. Lead and slug cutter

5-3. Trimmer saw

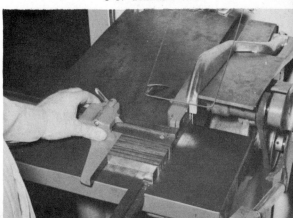

5-4. Typical paper drill

picas, with a micrometer adjustment to permit settings to ½ point. The trimmer saw is found in most commercial printing plants (5-3).

Paper Drill

When a job requires holes penetrating many sheets of paper, the paper drill is recommended (5-4).

The paper drill consists of a power-driven hollow drill, with provision made for forcing the drill through the paper stock. The stock table is usually raised to the drill by a foot lever. Adjustable guides are provided for positioning the paper. The round portion drilled from the sheet is forced through the hollow point drill into a receptacle.

This machine replaces the hand-operated paper punch.

Scoring

Scoring is striking a piece of paper with a rule at the folding point to make it fold easily and smoothly. A steel scoring rule is made which resembles the familiar brass rule. This is locked in a chase as though it were to be used for printing on a press. Rollers are removed from the press and the usual makeready procedure followed. Sufficient impression is used to make the paper fold easily. On heavy paper, this not only improves

the appearance of the fold but it also makes more accurate folds possible, whether folding is done by hand or machine. Paper folded by machine is frequently scored before the fold is made, in one operation.

Perforating

Perforating is similar to scoring, except that the rule is sharp and cuts an intermittent line across the sheet, which makes it possible to tear the sheet at the point of perforation. For very short runs, perforating may be done on an ordinary drawsheet with hard packing, if the drawsheet is reinforced on the underside with a strip of tape where the rule strikes it. Steel jackets, available for all presses, are recommended for extensive perforating. A suitable substitute, for the occasional job, is a flat sheet of aluminum placed under the drawsheet. The drawsheet is cut out where the perforating rule strikes it and glued or taped to the aluminum sheet to keep it from tearing.

Machines are also specifically designed for perforating. They are available in small hand-operated as well as power models.

Die Cutting

Die cutting is similar to perforating and scoring on a press, in that a special steel rule with a sharp edge is employed. A steel jacket or plate is recommended as a surface to cut against. The cutting rule is bent to conform to the design desired and usually held in place by a saw kerf in a piece of ¾″ plywood. Sponge rubber slightly higher than the rule is glued to the plywood in spots throughout the form, which forces the paper away from the rule after the impression has been made.

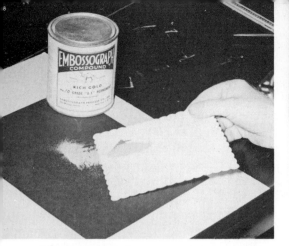

5-5. Apply powder to printing

5-6. Remove excess powder

Sharp bends are difficult to make without special bending equipment. Several companies specialize in making up die forms for the printing industry.

Thermography

Thermography, sometimes referred to as "fried" printing, is employed to simulate engraving (raised printing) and therefore is known as imitation engraving. This process raises the printed surface by heating a special powder dusted onto wet ink. Thermography powder is available in neutral, which imparts the color of the ink, as well as copper, gold, and silver.

A special powder is dusted onto wet ink (5-5), the excess powder is removed (5-6), and the sheet is then placed under heat until the powder fuses (5-7). The result is a raised surface (5-8).

Special machines for the applica-tion of the powder and heat make the process comparatively inexpensive in commercial printing. For short runs, an infra-red lamp as a source of heat works very well.

Rubber Stamps

Rubber stamps are vulcanized in plastic molds of lines of type or relief plates. The kind of plastic used becomes soft when heated to 200° F., then hard upon the continued application of heat.

Although regular printers type can be used for rubber stamp making, brass type is more satisfactory because it is more durable and the counters are cut deeper. Any type used for making rubber stamps should not be used for any other purpose, because heat affects it adversely. After type has been set, proofed, and corrected, type-high "bearer" strips (to bear the pressure

5-7. Apply heat to printing

5-8. Raised printing

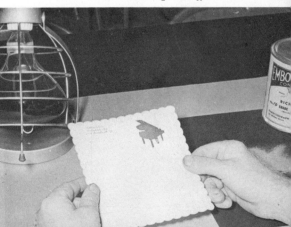

5-9. Type form locked in chase

In making the mold, preheat the type form for two minutes by sliding the chase into the press, which has been heated to 300° F (5-10).

Remove the chase and place a piece of plastic molding material with the *red side* against the type. Cover the back of the bakelite with paper to prevent it from sticking to the heated platen (5-11).

Insert the type form with the plastic mold and paper into the press. Raise the bed by turning the hand wheel clockwise until the first resistance is felt. Resistance indicates that

and hold type in place), about 12 points thick and of a measure equal to that of the type lines, is placed above and below the type. Separate the bearers from the type by 12 point slugs. See the illustration.

Type is locked near the center of the special chase. The limit stops on the chase should be *up*. Metal furniture is used for lockup because the heat generated in the stamp press will dry out and shrink wood furniture.

5-11. Place plastic over type

5-10. Slide form into press for pre-heating

5-12. Turn handwheel clockwise

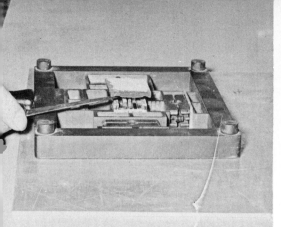

5-13. Pry matrix from type form

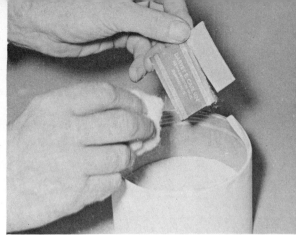

5-14. Dust matrix and stamp gum with soapstone

the plastic is in contact with the heated platen. As previously said, the molding material becomes soft at about 200° F. but, when heated to 300° F. for ten minutes, becomes hard and will remain hard whether heated more or cooled to room temperature.

After the plastic has been in contact with the heated platen for one minute, the bed is raised to the extent allowed by the limit stops on the chase (5-12).

After the mold has baked for ten minutes, the chase and mold are removed from the press. Since the chase is hot, it is placed on an unpainted metal surface. Then carefully pry the matrix from the type form (5-13).

Cut a piece of stamp gum about ⅛" larger than the type area. Dust both the gum and matrix with soapstone. Be sure to remove all excess powder from the mold cavities (5-14).

Place the matrix, mold side upward, on the vulcanizing tray. Then place the stamp gum face down directly over the cavity in the matrix. Cover the stamp gum with a piece of paper (5-15), and slide the vulcanizing tray into the stamp press. Raise the bed by turning the hand wheel clockwise to the full extent allowed by the limit bars on the vulcanizing tray. After six minutes, the stamp gum will

be vulcanized and the tray can be removed from the press by turning the hand wheel counterclockwise.

After the matrix has cooled, strip the vulcanized rubber from the matrix (5-16).

The stamp is properly vulcanized if no permanent mark is left when the thumbnail is pressed into the type face. Examine the stamp carefully to make sure the letters are clear and sharp. If a defect is discovered, examine the mold carefully and, if the mold is in good condition, another stamp can be vulcanized from the same matrix (5-17).

Trim the vulcanized stamp as close to the raised printing surface as possible. Taper the cut away from the printing surface for best results (5-18).

5-15. Matrix and stamp gum

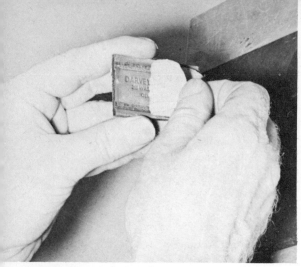

5-16. Strip vulcanized stamp from mold.

5-17. Test stamp for proper vulcanization

Moldings for mounting stamps are available from suppliers in strips 24 inches in length and in widths from ¼ inch upward. Select a molding that is just wide enough to accommodate the stamp. Cut it to length, not to exceed the length of the longest line by more than $\frac{1}{16}$ inch (5-19).

Sand the ends of the mounting strip and give a coat of stain to match the finish of the molding. Attach the stamp to the sponge rubber of the mounting strip with rubber cement. Take care that the stamp is straight on the mounting strip.

With stamp pad and paper, make a trial impression of stamp and inspect for defects. The trial stamping may then be trimmed so that it can be inserted under the plastic coating on the mounting strip, which will identify the subject (5-20).

Rubber stamps are mounted on type-high wood or metal blocks. These blocks may be locked in a type form used for printing on a conventional letter press.

Such stamps are frequently used to print envelopes, or to print on wood or metal surfaces.

A school model rubber stamp press has been used for this presentation. However, the procedure and materials used in making rubber stamps is similar for commercial presses.

5-18. Trim excess rubber from stamp

5-19. Prepare molding for stamp

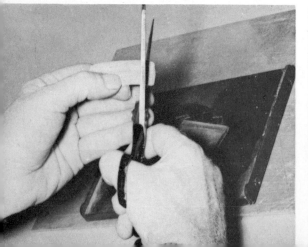

5-20. Completed stamp

Hot Stamping

Hot stamping was first introduced in Germany in 1905. It was referred to as imitation gold leaf or bronze stamping, since these were the materials first used. The process grew rapidly and was used extensively in bookbinding, partially replacing the use of gold leaf for pressing into leather covers.

Imitation foils for hot stamping have been perfected which resemble gold and silver, and are also available in a range of colors.

Hot stamping is now not only popular for decorating fine book covers but is also used to imprint other leather goods, book matches, napkins, stationery, wood products, cloth, and plastics.

Heat and pressure are used in this process. Brass type is recommended because it is more durable under heat and pressure than lead type. If stand-

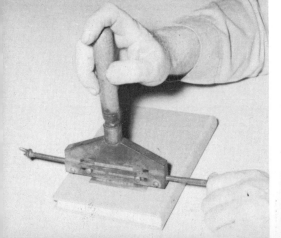

5-21. Hand pallet

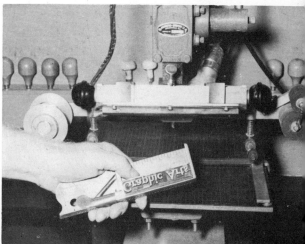

5-22. Set type in composing stick

ard lead type is used, it should not be used for any other purpose, because the heat and pressure affect it, making it unsatisfactory for letterpress printing.

The simplest device for hot stamping is the hand pallet (5-17). Type is set and placed in the pallet, which may be heated over a hot plate. The foil is positioned and, when heated to about 300°F., the type, held by the pallet, is pressed against the foil, which will cling to the surface being stamped. Considerable practice and skill are required to make good prints. The process is slow and is practical for the beginner if only a single stamping is required.

Hot stamping presses are available, on which the pallet heat is thermostatically controlled. The type holder is rigidly positioned when lowered with the hand lever, and the bed provides accurate guides for positioning material to be stamped. The foil is held in position below the type holder and may be adjusted for automatic movement after each stamp has been made.

Type for hot stamping is set in a composing stick with a slug on each side of line or lines of type (5-22).

Rest the composing stick on the bed of the press in front of the type holder (5-23).

5-23. Place composing stick on bed of press

Position the type in the type holder with nicks upward; tighten the clamps pressing against each end. Then tighten the thumbscrew to the slug which is against the side of the line (5-24).

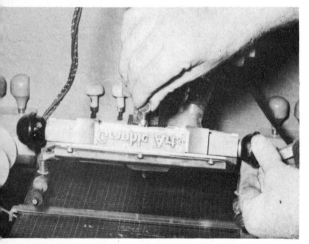

5-24. Transfer type to type holder

5-25. Move pallet to operating position

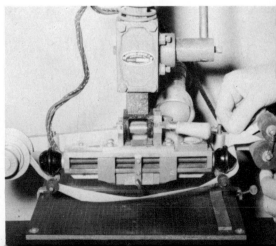

5-26. Lock pallet in operating position

Hold the pallet with the left hand on the plastic knob, releasing the lock with the right hand. (Reverse if left-handed.) Lower the pallet to a vertical position (5-25).

When the pallet is in a vertical position, the face of the type will be toward the base of the press. Lock the pallet in this position (5-26).

Place the roll of foil on the spindle at the left of the press (5-27). The "bright" side of the foil is up when threaded through the guides under the type. Place the end of the foil between the two rubber rollers on the right side of the press. The foil may be fed through the press by manually turning the rubber rolls. When several impressions are to be made of the same type form, the automatic roll feed is adjusted by means of the knurled bushing on top of the steel rack directly behind the type holder.

5-27. Thread foil

5-28. Turn on heat

5-30. Stamping a cover

Plug into electric socket and then turn the switch on top of the machine to "high" (5-28). After about ten minutes, turn the switch back to "medium." This heat may be used except for hard plastics, which require high heat.

The table of the press is marked with horizontal and vertical lines. These are used in positioning the guides. Make a trial stamp on chipboard or similar material. Check location and squareness.

After the guides have been properly adjusted, practice stamping on scraps of the kind of material that is to be stamped. There are two variables which must be considered for each individual job: (1) the amount of pressure to be exerted on the handle which brings the pallet down, (2) the length of time the type is held in contact with the material being stamped. Usually about two pounds pressure exerted on the handle for a period of one second is sufficient. However, make several stampings, varying pressure and time, and select the one giving best results. Remember, different materials may alter both of these factors.

Place material to be stamped to the guides. Hold material with the left hand, bringing the lever down with the right hand (5-30). Examine the stamping before removing the material. If an inadequate deposit of foil has been made, the operation may be repeated, provided the material has not been moved.

Immediately after stamping has been completed, and the type is still hot, clean the type face with a soft wiping cloth, as in the illustration below.

5-29. Adjust guides

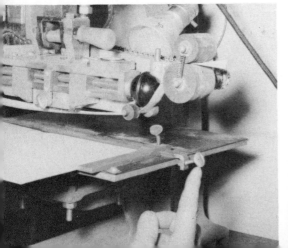

5-31. Clean type

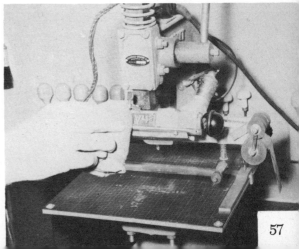

Stock Sizes and Weights

Paper stock is sold by paper suppliers in large sheets so that the printer can cut special sizes from the larger units, which provides an almost limitless range of sizes and reduces the amount of waste.

Paper is sold by weight with the exception of cardboard and chipboard, which is sold by the sheet. Sizes are always specified in inches; thickness is designated on the basis of weight per ream of 500 sheets of a given size or on the basis of 1000 sheets of a given size. Cardboard and chipboard weights are designated by sheets per bundle or by ply number. This book is printed on book paper, basic weight 60 pounds. This means one ream of book paper 25 x 38 inches (which is basic size for book paper) weighs 60 pounds. If the paper was cut from a larger sheet, the weight of a ream would be proportionately greater, but the *basic* weight would still be 60 pounds, since all book paper is designated according to the basic 25 x 38 inch size.

Basic sizes vary with different kinds of paper. For example the basic size for bond paper is 17 x 22, index bristol 25½ x 30½, cover paper 20 x 26, etc. Basic sizes and weights available are listed in paper supply catalogs.

If 860 pieces of stock 8½ x 11 is required for a job and is to be cut from a sheet size 25 x 38, how many large sheets would be needed? First, find the number of pieces that could be cut from one sheet of paper by dividing the width and length or the piece into width and length of sheet.

$$2 \times 4 = 8$$
$$25 \times 38$$
$$8\tfrac{1}{2} \times 11$$
$$2 \times 3 = 6$$

38 divided by 8½ equal 4
25 divided by 11 equal 2
2 × 4 equal 8 pieces per sheet

The other way of cutting the sheet would be:

38 divided by 11 equal 3
25 divided by 8½ equal 2
2 × 3 equal 6 pieces per sheet

The first way would, of course, result in the least amount of waste and be the most economical method. Since 8 pieces could be cut per sheet, and 860 pieces are required for the job, divide 860 by 8, which equals 107½ large sheets.

In figuring stock, if a fraction of a sheet is required, include the full sheet anyway; in this case, 108 sheets, 25 x 38, would be required to cut 860 pieces 8½ x 11.

Cutting Paper

The paper cutter is designed to cut large sheets into desired size accu-

5-32. Paper cutter

rately and with ease (5-32). Most graphic art centers are equipped with hand lever cutters, although commercial plants usually have power driven cutters, many with automatic clamping devices.

Sheets of paper to be cut are placed on the bed of the cutter and are jogged to the back fence and the left side guide. The hand wheel below the bed in front of the cutter controls the back fence. If the cutter is not equipped with a steel tape which indicates how many inches the back fence is from the cutter blade, a soft basswood yardstick is recommended to set the back fence. Rest the yardstick against the back fence and read the measurement where it coincides with the front of the clamp immedi-

ately behind the knife blade. After the back fence has been set and the paper accurately jogged to the back fence and side guide, clamp the paper tightly in this position by revolving the large hand wheel on top of the cutter frame. The knife is then brought down. Most cutters are equipped with a safety device which requires both hands on the lever.

Although the cutter blade is razor sharp, smoother cuts will result if the blade is brought down in one sweeping motion rather than by hacking.

After the cut has been made, raise the hand lever to its normal position, unclamp the stock, and reset the cutter for the next cut. *Under no circumstances should you operate the paper cutter with another person.*

Sample Tests—Chapter 5

Completion

Directions: Words or phrases have been omitted from the following statements. Fill in the proper word or phrase to make the statement complete and correct.

Example: 1. The paper cutter is designed to cut   paper

1. The lead and slug cutter is adjustable to _____ and _____ _____ measures and is designed for cutting leads and slugs.

2. The paper drill replaces the common hand operated _____ _____.

3. A _____ material is used to make molds for rubber stamps.

4. Brass type is recommended for hot stamping because it is more durable and will withstand _____ and _____ much better than ordinary printers type.

5. Paper is sold by weight with the exception of _____ and _____.

True-False

Directions: The following statements are either true or false. If the statement is true, circle the "T" at the left of the numbered item. If the statement is false, circle the "F".

Example: Ⓣ F 1. Sheets are perforated to make them tear easily at the point of perforation.

T F 6. Thermography simulates engraving.

T F 7. More than one rubber stamp can be vulcanized from one mold.

T F 8. Rubber stamps mounted on type high blocks can be used for printing on a platen press.

T F 9. Regular printers type works better than other kinds of type for hot stamping.

T F 10. Book paper is ordered according to ream weight based on 60 pound stock, size 25 x 38

Matching

Directions: The words or phrases in the column on the right match one of the words or phrases in the column on the left. Place the letter preceding the matching word or phrase of the column on the right in the blank space provided in the column on the left.

Example: <u>a</u>   1. Hot Stamping   a. Foils

_____11. Folding   a. Thermography

_____12. Raised
        printing   b. Vulcanizing

_____13. Paper drill   c. Molding

_____14. Stamp
        gum   d. Scoring

_____15. Brass type   e. Holes

Multiple Choice

Directions: Following each statement there are several answers, only one of which is correct. Place the letter preceding the correct answer in the space provided on the left of the question.

Example: <u>b</u>   1. The paper drill is designed to (a) punch holes in paper (b) cut holes in paper (c) make perforation in paper.

_____16. To make paper fold easily and accurately, it is frequently necessary (a) to die cut the paper (b) to dampen the paper (c) to score the paper.

_____17. In order to do die cutting on a platen press it is necessary to (a) raise the platen on the press (b) lower the platen on the press (c) remove the rollers from the press.

_____18. In molding matrixes for rubber stamps it is necessary to heat the material to 300°F. for (a) ten minutes (b) six minutes (c) two minutes.

_____19. The matrix used for making rubber stamps should be dusted with soapstone (a) before the matrix is molded (b) before the stamp is vulcanized (c) after the stamp has been vulcanized.

_____20. Hot stamping was first introduced in Germany in (a) 1905 (a) 1805 (c) 1705.

Chapter 6

SILK SCREEN

SILK SCREEN printing is a form of stencil printing using a design cut out of paper, or other material, attached to a sheet of silk which has been tightly stretched across a frame. Ink is then forced through the open meshes of the silk by means of a rubber blade called a squeegee.

Although much material is now being printed with a simple wooden frame and a hand squeegee, elaborate and complex printing units have been devised during the last decade. This has made the process practical for designs to be reproduced in great volume.

The silk screen printing process is versatile. It is practical for short runs because of the low cost in the preparation for printing. It is also practical for long runs when automatic equipment is employed. Not only is it adapted to short and long runs, but it is also possible to print a design of almost any size on any surface, such as wood, metal, fabrics, and plastics, as well as on many kinds of paper. Since a heavy deposit of ink is possible, it is especially well adapted to printing reflective signs and displays.

Silk is the most popular fabric. However, cotton organdy, nylon, and fine wire mesh screens are good for special uses. The size opening in the mesh might vary from 6xx (coarse) to 18xx (very fine) in silk. Medium or 10xx is recommended for average work. Coarse mesh is used for big, heavy designs and the finer meshes for smaller, detailed work. Fine mesh is recommended for printing photographic stencils. See later discussion. Photographic stencils must be used for reproduction of halftones by the silk screen process.

The simplest stencil would be a silhouette design cut in a piece of paper. However, hand cut film stencils are more practical when there are loose centers in the design. Tusche and crayon stencils are preferred for scenics and poster reproduction.

The general procedure is similar for all types of stencils. First, the design must be made; second, the printing unit is prepared for printing; third, the stencil is prepared and fastened to the silk; fourth is the printing operation; and fifth, the printing unit is cleaned.

Preparation of Design

The design to be printed is prepared in full size and the different colors are clearly indicated. Color the design exactly as you expect it to be reproduced.

The original design is either made on the size paper it is to be reproduced on, or mounted on paper cut to the size that will be printed.

Preparation of Printing Unit

The silk on the printing frame must be perfectly clean and free from

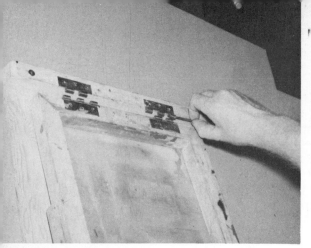

6-1. Remove printing frame from base

6-2. Pull cord from groove

clogged areas where the design to be printed is attached. Check for clogged areas by holding the screen up to a light source. Frequently a small clogged area can be cleaned out with water or an ink solvent.

The screen should also be checked to make sure there are no holes or "runs." Even slight blemishes in the silk will show up on the printing. It is also important to handle screens carefully to prevent damage to the silk. A good grade of silk may be used many times if it is properly cleaned upon completion of the printing operation.

To replace the silk on a printing frame, remove the frame from the base (6-1). The pins can be pulled from the hinges which hold the frame to the base.

Silk may be secured to the frame by a cord which has been forced into a groove on top of the silk (6-2). An edged instrument such as a screw driver or knife is used to "start" the end of the cord, making it easier to pull it from the groove.

The silk is easily stripped from the frame after the cord has been removed (6-3). Examine the frame and remove any sharp edges which would contact the silk.

Cut a piece of silk about the same

6-3. Remove old silk from frame

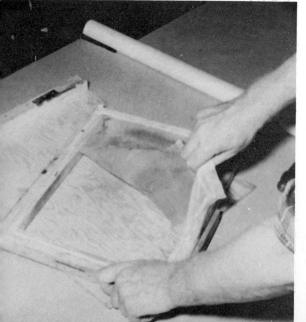

6-4. Cut new silk to fit frame

6-5. Start cord in groove over silk

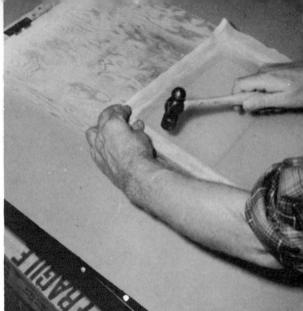

6-6. Tap cord down

size as the outside dimension of the frame (6-4).

Lay the silk over the frame and press the cord over the silk into the groove with finger pressure (6-5).

After the cord has been tucked lightly in the groove, examine the silk to make sure it is properly positioned and free from wrinkles. Tap the cord down into the groove with a hammer so the cord is even with the top of the frame (6-6).

Use a thin piece of wood to drive the cord deeper into the groove (6-7). It may be necessary to go around the frame in this manner several times in order to tighten the silk. It is better to drive the cord a small amount each time around than to drive the cord to the bottom of the groove all at one time. A uniformly tight silk is important in order to make clear, sharp prints.

Tightening fluid, called "silk tight," or airplane "dope," is applied on the cord and silk extending over the inside edge of the frame about ½ inch (6-8).

After the silk tight is thoroughly dry, wash the silk with clean warm water (6-9). This removes the starch from the cloth.

Cut a piece of wrapping paper equal to the length of the base and about 8 inches wider (6-10). Stretch the paper over the base of the frame

6-7. Stretch silk

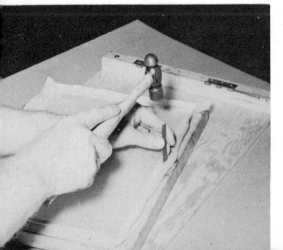

6-8. Apply silk tight

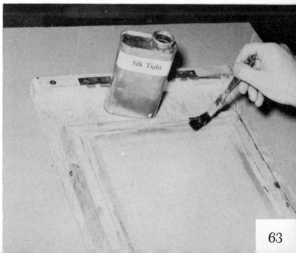

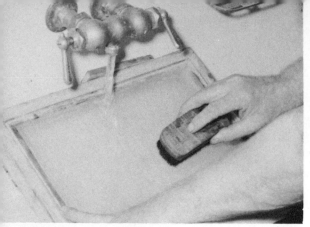

6-9. Wash silk

6-12. Insert sheets to build up base under screen

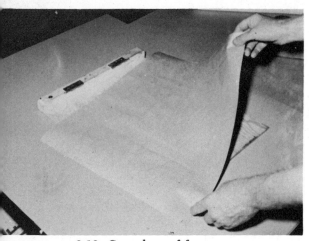

6-10. Cover base of frame

6-13. Attach frame to base

and attach it with gum tape to the underside of the base (6-11).

The silk of the frame must fully contact the base (6-13). It may be necessary to insert sheets of paper between the base and the covering sheet

in order to bring the silk in good contact with the base (6-12).

The frame again is attached to the base by inserting the pins in the hinges (6-13). The unit is now ready to be set up for printing.

Paper Stencil

Kraft wrapping paper or a lightweight bond paper may be used for making paper stencils. The paper is cut to a size equal to the outside dimensions of the silk screen frame.

Trace the design onto the paper from which the stencil is to be made. With a sharp knife, on a smooth hard surface, cut out the design (6-14).

6-11. Tape covering to underside of base

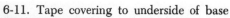

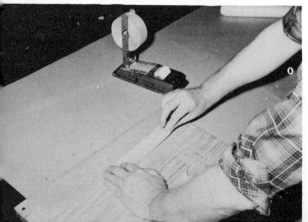

64

6-14. Cut design out of paper

6-17. Glue stencil in position

6-15. Locate register guides

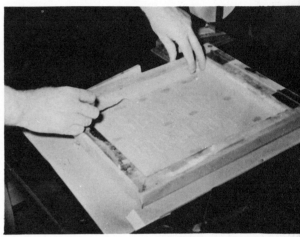

6-18. Mask corners of frame

This type of stencil is not recommended for designs which have loose centers, such as the inside of the letter "o."

Place the original design on the

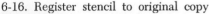

6-16. Register stencil to original copy

base of the printing frame mounted on paper which is the same size as the object to be printed. Attach three guide strips to the base of the frame with tape. Locate two guides on the long edge and one guide on the short edge toward the hinge end of the base (6-15).

Place the stencil in register over the original copy (6-16). Lower the frame, being careful not to permit the stencil to slip from this position.

Then place several spots of ordinary glue on the silk, to hold the stencil in position while printing (6-17).

With gummed kraft tape, mask the corners of the screen printing frame

6-19. Printing

6-20. Printed copy

to prevent ink from accumulating in these corners (6-18).

The printing operation (6-19), handling printed copies (6-20), and cleaning the frame when the printing operation have been completed are explained in detail on page 74.

Hand Cut Film Stencil

Hand cut film stencils are commonly used in school and home practice.

Film stencils are made of a thin film of gelatinous material on a wax paper or plastic backing. The gelatinous material is cut and stripped from the backing sheet according to the design. This material is transparent, so the design may be taped to the back of the film. The film may be soluble in water, which means that the gelatinous material becomes soft when it is moistened with water. This makes it

possible for it to adhere to the silk.

Lacquer films are soluble only in lacquer thinner. The type of film selected will depend upon the type of ink to be used for printing. If water colors are used, a lacquer film is required; with lacquer inks, use a water soluble film.

Cut the film to a size that will provide a 2 inch margin all around the design. Attach the design to the back of the film and secure with tape (6-21).

A sharp knife is very important in cutting film. Do the cutting on a hard, smooth surface, such as pressed board or glass. Use a very light pressure. Cut *only* through the gelatinous film.

Remove the film from the backing sheet *only in the areas to be printed.* Use the point of the knife to lift the film so it can be peeled off from the backing sheet (6-22). In cutting sharp corners, the knife cut may ex-

6-21. Attach design to film

6-22. Peel film from backing

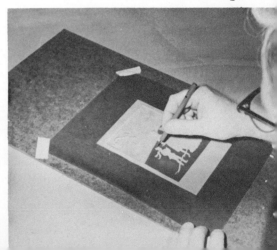

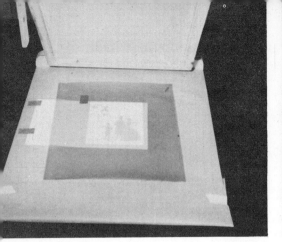

6-23. Locate guides on base

6-24. Adhere water soluble stencil

tend beyond the corners. When the film adheres to the silk, the small opening left by the knife cut beyond the corners will seal itself and will not print.

After the film has been cut, check it carefully to make sure no part has been missed. Remove the design from the back of the film and examine the backing sheet. The backing sheet should not be embossed from the pressure of the knife in cutting the film. Even slight evidence of knife pressure on the backing sheet makes it impossible for the film to adhere to the silk. It is recommended that beginners do some practice cutting before the design cutting is started. Only in this way is it possible to become familiar with the pressure required to cut the film—yet not to emboss the backing sheet.

The same technique is used in cutting either water soluble or lacquer soluble stencil films.

Locate register guides on the base of the printing unit (6-23). Place the cut stencil in register with the original copy on the base of the printing unit. Lower the screen frame onto the stencil, which is then adhered to the silk.

Make certain the silk is clean—free of paint, dust, or dirt—before starting. Thoroughly moisten the silk with a wet cloth. Place the silk over stencil, making sure that perfect contact is obtained over the entire area. It is best to use a solid, smooth "build-up" on the base of the frame to accomplish this. Hard, waterproof material, either glass or metal, smaller than the frame itself, will assure best results.

When the dampened silk has been properly placed over the stencil, take a well saturated cloth and thoroughly wet a 12 inch square area of the stencil (6-24). With an absorbent, soft, dry cloth, wipe up the excess moisture from the saturated area in a firm, rubbing motion. Work 12 inch square areas of the stencil at a time. Repeat this same procedure until entire stencil has been covered.

Stencils darken in color with wetting. If a stencil shows a lighter color in spots, it is an indication of poor adhesion. To correct, merely redampen and follow instructions for adhering.

6-25. Peel backing paper from stencil

6-26. Remove water soluble stencil

6-27. Remove lacquer stencil

A fan may be used to accelerate drying. Normal drying time is about fifteen minutes. At this point, the backing sheet is ready for removal. Pick up a corner and peel off the entire backing sheet (6-25).

While the stencil is still damp and drying, the silk side of the frame will feel cool to the hand because of the water evaporation taking place. A good check before pulling off the backing sheet is to see if the stencil feels as warm as other surfaces. At normal room temperature, a stencil is dry.

Remove the screen frame from the base of the printing unit. Brush both sides of the silk with water, using a stiff bristle brush to insure thorough wetting (6-26). Let the wet stencil stand for 5 to 10 minutes. Then flush off on stencil side with either hot or cold water. Faster removal will result if hot water is used.

Lacquer soluble film is adhered in a similar manner to the water soluble film. However, lacquer thinner must be used to soften the gelatinous material. It is recommended that smaller areas be adhered at one time because of the rapid evaporation of the lacquer thinner. Lacquer thinner has a low flash point, therefore it should not be used in the presence of an open flame. The room should be well ventilated.

To remove a lacquer film after printing, place several layers of old newspapers under the screen frame. Pour a small puddle of lacquer thinner on the stencil inside the frame. Let this stand from three to five minutes. Lift the frame from the newsprint (6-27). Most of the lacquer film will be pulled from the silk and will stick to the newsprint. Repeat this operation until about 95 per cent of the lacquer film has been removed

6-28. Trace design on silk

6-29. Apply liquid tusche

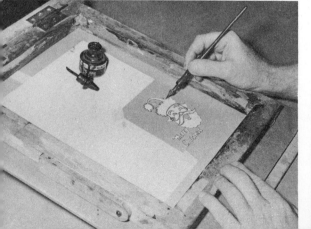

6-30. Spread glue over silk

6-31. Wash out liquid tusche

from the silk. The remainder can be removed with a wiping cloth moistened with lacquer thinner.

Tusche Stencil

In making this type of stencil, the design is applied directly to the silk with liquid tusche or a lithographic crayon. Glue is squeegeed over the silk and, when dry, the design made with tusche or crayon is washed out with mineral spirits.

Locate the guides to be used to position the paper to be printed on the base of the unit. Position the design to the guides and drop the screen frame on top of the design.

In this position, the design will be visible through the silk. Trace the design onto the silk with India ink (6-28).

Solid areas are covered with liquid tusche applied with a brush (6-29). A No. 5 lithographic pencil may be

used to fill in the shaded areas. Fine lines may also be drawn with a ruling pen and liquid tusche, and in some cases an ordinary pen can be used to advantage. Care must be exercised not to snag the silk.

After the tusche is dry, remove the frame from the base and elevate the frame with a strip of wood under each end.

Pour a small quantity of engravers' glue, which has been diluted with 35 per cent water and 5 per cent vinegar, inside the frame. With a strip of cardboard, squeegee the glue over the silk, including the design area (6-30). This must dry in an elevated position.

The design made with liquid tusche or lithographic crayon may now be washed out of the silk with mineral spirits (6-31). A soft bristle brush is good for this operation.

The glue is not soluble in mineral

6-32. Completed stencil

6-33. Remove glue stencil

spirits, so the only portion that will wash out is the design (6-32). Open areas in the screen frame may now be blocked out in preparation for printing.

After printing, stencils made with tusche and glue can be washed out of the silk with warm water (6-33).

Photographic Stencils

The rapid growth of the silk screen process can be attributed in a large measure to the development and perfection of the photographic method in making silk screen stencils. This, like all photography, is based upon the principle that substances such as gelatin or albumen will become *light sensitive* when mixed with salts such as sodium, potassium, or ammonium bichromate. When a substance has been made light sensitive, it will harden when exposed to light. Areas protected from light remain soft.

There are two types of photographic stencils being used—the direct type and the transfer type. In the direct type, the silk or other fabric is sensitized with an emulsion directly on the screen. The transfer type of photographic stencil is first processed and then transferred to the screen.

Since less elaborate equipment is required to make photographic transfer stencils, this process is recommended for small operations. There are several different methods in making transfer stencils photographically. Some do not even require dark room facilities. Here a pigment paper type of photographic stencil is explained in detail. However, the same principles apply for all photographic transfer stencils.

A transparent positive of the design is the first requirement. A trans-

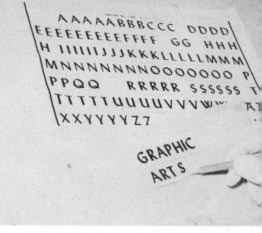

6-34. Artype letters for positive

parent positive is an opaque design on a transparent sheet. Positives can be made by photographing the design with auto-positive film. Positives can also be made by drawing the design on a matte finish acetate, or a good grade of tracing paper commonly used by draftsmen.

Transparent positives can also be made by pasting artype letters on transparent acetate (6-34). The artype letters are printed with black ink on a thin plastic material which has a sticky back. The line below the letter is cut out with the letter from the sheet and is used to align the letters on the acetate. This guide line is cut off after the word or words have been assembled.

When the positive has been prepared, mount the original design on paper which is the size of paper or other material to be printed. This is

6-35. Locate guides on base

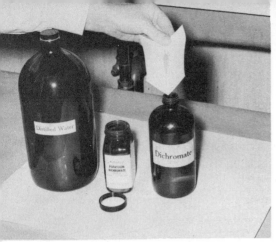

6-36. Mix sensitizing solution

6-39. Pour dichromate into tray

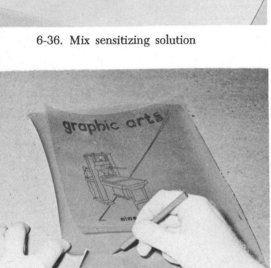

6-37. Cut pigment paper

used to locate register guides. Guides may be made of index bristol and taped to the base of the frame (6-35). Whenever possible, use two guides on the long edge of the sheet and one

guide on the short edge toward the hinges of the printing frame.

Dissolve 2½ ounces·of potassium dichromate into 1 gallon of cool distilled water (6-36). The crystals must be completely dissolved.

Cut a piece of pigment paper about 2 inches larger on all edges than the design (6-37).

Cut a piece of clear vinylite, which is about .003″ thick, slightly larger than the pigment paper (6-38).

Pour the dichromate into the developing tray to depth of at least ½ inch (6-39).

Immerse pigment paper into the tray of dichromate. The pigment side is upward. Hold the pigment paper under the surface until the paper becomes soft and lies flat (6-40).

When air bubbles appear on the pigment, it is not absorbing the sensi-

6-38. Cut Vinylite

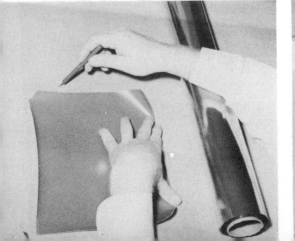

6-40. Immerse pigment paper in dichromate

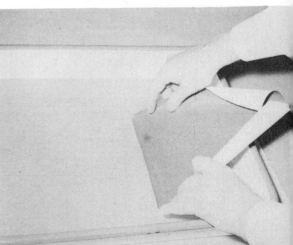

6-41. Remove air bubbles

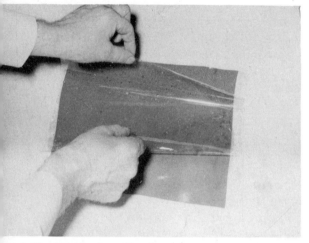

6-42. Attach clear Vinylite to pigment paper

tizing solution in that particular spot. With the finger, or a soft brush, rub the surface of the pigment lightly to remove the bubble (6-41). The pigment paper is then left in the solution from two to three minutes.

6-43. Press Vinylite to pigment paper

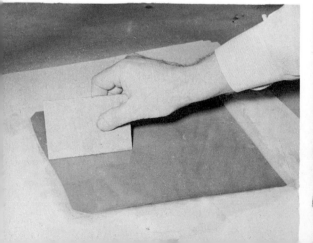

6-44. Pigment paper in exposure frame

Rinse the clear vinylite in cold water and attach to the pigment side of the pigment paper. Start in the center and roll the vinylite onto the pigment (6-42).

Use an oblong piece of stiff cardboard or a photographic roller to press the vinylite to the pigment (6-43). Pockets of air must be worked to the outer edges. A small air bubble between vinylite and pigment results in a pinhole in the stencil.

The vinylite, attached to the pigment paper, will serve as a carrying medium to transfer the completed stencil to the silk.

Place a piece of clean paper over the mat of the exposure frame, on which the pigment paper is placed with the vinylite on top (6-44).

Place the transparent positive face down on the vinylite (6-45). Center the positive, to have equal margins.

6-45. Transparent positive in position

6-46. Expose sensitized pigment paper

6-48. Wash out stencil

The light source should be at least 2½ feet from the exposure frame (6-46). At this distance, exposure time is about ten minutes when a No. 2 photoflood lamp is used.

The exposure frame or device can be very simple, such as clamping the pigment paper and positive together between two sheets of glass. The important point to keep in mind is that the positive must make good contact with the pigment paper. Exposure may be made in sunlight, although it is more difficult to control the exposure time.

After the pigment paper has been exposed, the vinylite support, together with the pigment paper, is inserted in a tray of warm water (about 110°F.). In about 1½ minutes, the colored pigment will begin to ooze at the edges. At this point, strip the backing paper from the pigment

(6-47). Most of the pigment will stick to the clear vinylite, which will serve as a temporary support.

Discard the backing paper and place the vinylite, with the pigment side up, into the tray of warm water. Agitate the water by rocking the tray gently until the unexposed parts of the pigment are dissolved away.

When the design is clear, immerse the stencil in a tray of cool water (65° to 70°F.) for about two minutes (6-49).

Place the vinylite on soft paper, such as newsprint, to absorb water from the back of the stencil. Place the stencil in register with the design on the base of the printing frame (6-50).

Lower the screen frame onto the stencil. Place a piece of blotting paper, or newspaper, over the stencil and gently rub, which forces the soft

6-47. Remove backing paper from pigment

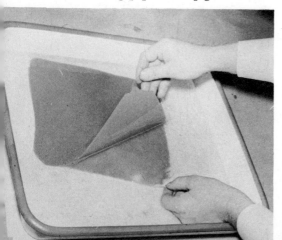

6-49. Rinse in cool water

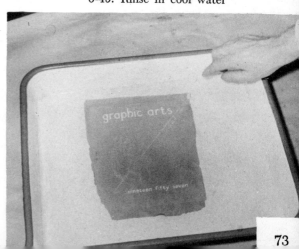

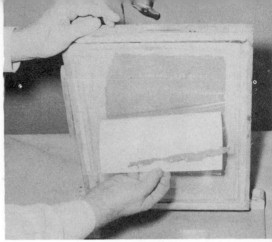

6-50. Register stencil with copy

6-52. Remove Vinylite

pigment into the meshes of the silk. Keep the blotting paper in one position.

It will take about thirty minutes for the pigment to dry in the meshes of the screen. This can be hastened by the application of heat. When the pigment and screen are thoroughly dry, the vinylite temporary support will fall off, or it may be peeled off, leaving the pigment in the screen (6-52). The remaining open areas in the screen may be masked or blocked out, and the screen is ready for printing.

To remove photographic stencils from a screen, detach the base from the frame. Soak the stencil in warm water for about three minutes; then brush the stencil, flushing away the pigment with warm water (6-53).

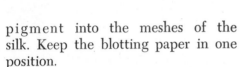

6-53. Remove photographic stencil

Silk Screen Printing

Procedures are the same for printing from the various kinds of stencils. The kind of ink to be used is determined by the kind of material to be

6-51. Adhere stencil to screen

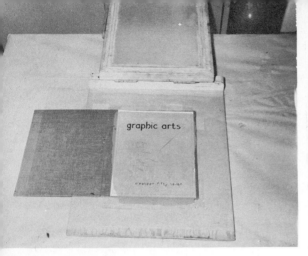

6-54. Fit mask to frame

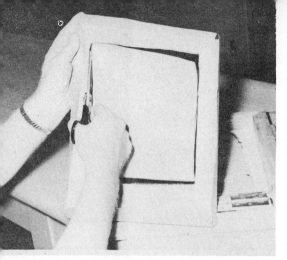

6-55. Cut opening in mask

6-57. Place ink in screen frame

printed. Silk screen supply houses stock special inks for a wide variety of printing surfaces. In most small plants and school laboratories, the ink stock consists of an assortment of oil-base colors for regular work and perhaps an assortment of colored inks for textile printing.

For limited budgets, it is recommended that the primary colors of blue, red, yellow, black, and white and mixing white be kept on hand. With this stock, other colors can be mixed.

In most cases the stencil does not cover all of the open areas of the screen. A paper mask, folded to fit the inside of the frame, is commonly used to cover these open areas (6-54).

By holding the screen and mask up to a light source, mark the mask where it must be cut out to permit printing the design (6-55).

Ordinary gummed paper tape is commonly used to seal the mask to the silk (6-56). Masking should be at least 1 inch away from the design on all edges. If masking is placed closer to the design, the squeegee does not make good contact with the silk, resulting in a fuzzy print.

Use a spatula to place a quantity of ink in the screen frame (6-57). Sufficient ink should be used so that it will roll in front of the squeegee, covering the design in one stroke.

The squeegee is held at a slight angle so that only the sharper edge of the rubber blade contacts the silk (6-58). With a firm downward pressure, pull the squeegee across the open areas in the screen. To get best results, use only one stroke to make one print. The squeegee should be wide enough to cover the area of the design. It is also important that the

6-56. Seal mask to silk

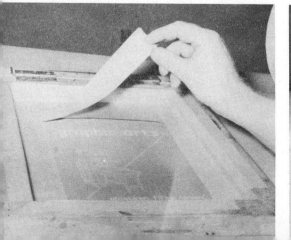

6-58. Hold squeegee at angle

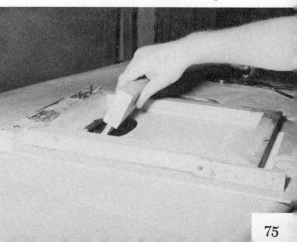

6-59. The printed cover

6-60. Remove ink from screen frame

rubber blade of the squeegee be straight, and the edges sharp. When the blade becomes rounded, it can be sharpened by drawing it back and forth over sandpaper, holding the squeegee in a vertical position.

Raise the screen frame, remove the printed copy, and insert another sheet to the register guides (6-59). Under normal conditions, without artificial heat, about thirty minutes is required for the ink to dry. Prints should be laid out singly in the drying rack. Do not stack them until they are dry.

Cleaning Screen Printing Frames

When the printing operation has been completed, clean the screen printing frame. Screens are most easily cleaned immediately after printing, before the ink dries in the meshes of the silk.

Use a piece of scrap cardboard to scrape up the ink remaining in the frame (6-60). Use an ink knife to push the ink from the cardboard back into the ink can (6-61). Do not scrape the ink knife on the edges of the can because it is necessary that the top edge of the can be kept clean so that the cover will fit tightly to prevent the ink from drying out.

After excess ink has been taken out of the screen frame, remove the masking paper and wrap in newspapers be-fore depositing in the wastepaper container (6-62).

Place several layers of newspapers under the screen printing frame. Saturate a wiping cloth with a solvent; then wash the silk and stencil on both sides (6-63). Screens properly cleaned after printing can be used for many stencils.

After all the ink has been removed from the screen and stencil, the stencil itself is removed (6-64). Under a previous description of the commonly used types of stencils, directions were also given for their removal. Generally one type of solvent is required for cleaning the ink from a screen and another solvent is required to remove the stencil. After the screen has been cleaned, and the stencil removed, hold the screen to a source of light to make sure no area is clogged. Expect the screen to be discolored from the ink, but the meshes should be open. If an area remains clogged, it is difficult to determine what causes it, ink or stencil film. For this reason, it is recommended that both types of solvent be tried in order to clean the clogged area.

The clean screen frame should be attached to the base (6-65). Remove the kraft paper from the base of the printing unit, which will indicate the unit is ready for another student.

6-61. Return surplus ink to container

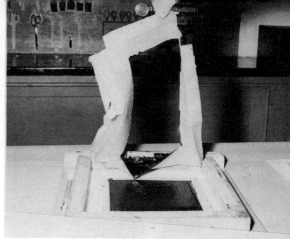

6-62. Remove masking paper

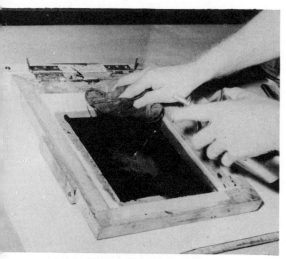

6-63. Wash silk and stencil

6-64. Remove stencil from screen

Sample Tests—Chapter 6

Completion

Directions: Words or phrases have been omitted from the following statements. Fill in the proper word or phrase to make the statement complete and correct.

Example: 1. Silk Screen printing is a form of __stencil__ printing.

1. In covering a silk screen frame with a new piece of silk, it is necessary to cut a piece of silk about the same size as the _____ dimension of the frame.

2. A new silk covering on a silk screen frame should be _____ before being used.

3. Six xx silk is considered a _____ mesh screen.

4. The squeegee should be held at a slight angle so that only the _____ _____ of the rubber blade contacts the silk.

5. The silk screen process is especially desirable for printing reflective signs because it is possible to make a _____ deposit of ink.

6-65. A clean screen

Multiple Choice

Directions: Following each statement there are several answers, only one of which is correct. Place the letter preceding the correct answer in the space provided on the left of the question.

Example: ___c___ 1. A squeegee is used to (a) open ink cans (b) cover ink cans (c) force paint through the screen.

_____ 6. Register guides should be located on the base of the screen frame (a) after the stencil has been attached to the screen (b) before the stencil has been attached to the screen (c) after the ink has been placed in the screen.

Matching

Directions: The words or phrases in the column on the right match one of the words or phrases in the column on the left. Place the letter preceding the matching word or phrase of the column on the right in the blank space provided in the column on the left.

Example: ___a___ 1. Squeegee   a. ink

_____11. Photographic   a. Heavy
            stencil   designs
_____12. Liquid   b. Glue
            tusche
_____13. Coarse mesh   c. Turpentine
            silk
_____14. Ink solvent   d. Copy
_____15. Register   e. Pigment
            stencil   paper

_____ 7. In order to print four separate colors by the silk screen process, it is necessary to prepare (a) two stencils (b) three stencils (c) four stencils.

_____ 8. Lacquer film stencils are adhered to the screen with (a) water (b) turpentine (c) lacquer thinner.

_____ 9. The backing sheet on film cut stencils should be removed (a) after the stencil is adhered to the screen (b) right after the stencil has been cut (c) before the stencil has been cut.

_____10. In making photographic transfer stencils, the clear vinylite is attached to the pigment paper (a) right after it has been exposed (b) right after it has been soaked in dichromate (c) right before being adhered to the screen.

True-False

Directions: The following statements are either true or false. If the statement is true, circle the "T" at the left of the numbered item. If the statement is false, circle the "F".

Example: Ⓣ F 1. Silk is commonly used to cover silk screen frames.

T F 16. In adhering water soluble film stencils, light colored areas indicate poor adhesion.

T F 17. Liquid tusche used to make stencils can be washed out with water.

T F 18. In making tusche and glue stencils, the glue is applied to the screen before the tusche is applied to the screen.

T F 19. A transparent positive is an opaque design on a transparent sheet.

T F 20. Six xx silk has a finer mesh than 18 xx silk.

Chapter 7

EVER SINCE paper and parchment have been used as writing materials, effort has been made to preserve these records. Early writings of the scribes were on long strips, with a wooden roller at each end, so the manuscript could be rolled as it was being read. When rolled up it was called a "volumen" and frequently enclosed in a wooden case for preservation. This was succeeded by folded leaves which were sewn together at the back edge to make double sheet "pages." The single leaf was a later development, which permitted writing on both sides rather than on just one side of the paper. Wooden covers, secured to the sewn leaves by cords, served to protect the enclosed pages. Bulky wooden covers were replaced by pasting several layers of paper together, forming a thin paper board. In order to make the new "boards" more durable, leather coverings were placed over the boards and around the back of the book. This proved most satisfactory and resembles the type of binding still being used. However, most mass produced volumes are enclosed in casings made of bookcloth, which is less expensive than leather. Plastic covering materials also are increasing in popularity because of their attractiveness and their superior wearing qualities.

In the manufacture of books today, there are very few hand operations. Elaborate machines and inexpensive materials have been developed which make it possible to bind printed ma-terials at a low unit cost. Progress has helped to make printed books available to people in all economic groups.

Hand binding is still practiced in the graphic arts industry where the number of any one volume is limited. For instance, magazines are frequently bound in book form for preservation as well as for making back issues readily available. Bookkeeping records are frequently bound into volumes at the end of the year for the same reason. Books which receive considerable handling, such as in public libraries, may be rebound to prolong their usefulness. Hand bookbinding is also a popular leisure-time activity. It is an interesting and useful craft which does not require elaborate equipment.

Padding, stapling, and stitching are bindery operations performed in almost all commercial printing plants. Although a brief introduction is given to these more common bindery operations, more emphasis has been placed upon the two major types of hand bookbinding. Signature binding is the type of binding common to most printed books. Loose sheet binding is used to secure sheets of paper together which have not been folded. The student who understands the basic principles of these two types of bindings has little difficulty in applying these principles to the rebinding of old books, or making a more permanent binding for paperbound volumes.

Padding

Pads are made by applying liquid rubber compound to the edge of sheets of paper which have been jogged evenly to one edge and placed under pressure. Special padding presses are available which are designed to make it easy to pad large quantities at one time.

For small quantities, place chipboard between each pad, and two pieces at the top and bottom of the pile to be padded. This is jogged evenly to the edge to be padded and placed under weights (7-1).

Padding compound is then applied lightly with a brush, working from the center of the pile to the outer edges (7-2). The first light coat dries in about twenty minutes. When the first coat has dried, apply a second coat, which will dry in about thirty minutes. The application of two light coats of padding compound is more satisfactory than the application of one heavy coat. Water soluble padding compound is recommended for school work centers. If padding compound is allowed to dry on the brush, it is impossible to clean it. Therefore wash out the brush with water immediately after use.

7-1. Pads under weights

7-2. Apply padding compound

7-3. Cut pads apart

After padding compound is dry, cut the pads apart, leaving one piece of chipboard at the bottom of each pad (7-3).

Trim the pads on the three exposed edges in order to make the pad look neat (7-4). When paper stock is cut

7-4. Trim pads on three sides

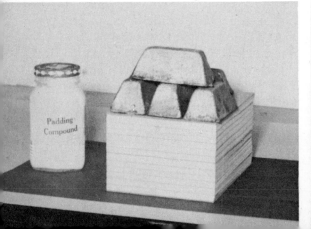

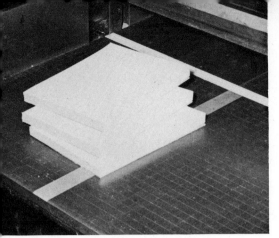

7-5. Completed pads

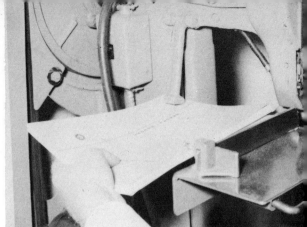

7-7. Booklet under thickness gauge

for jobs to be padded, an allowance of from ⅛ to ¼ inch should be made for trimming.

Stitching

Wire staples are commonly used to fasten sheets of paper together. Stapling machines are available in many different sizes, from hand models to large power machines. Such machines use ready-formed staples supplied in clips (7-6).

Paper stitching machines are dif-

7-6. Foot power stapler

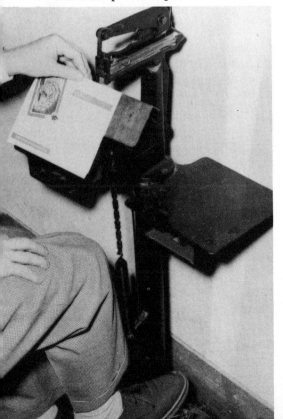

ferent from staplers in that the staple is formed by the machine from a spool of wire. The staples must be adjusted for the thickness of the job to be stapled.

Place the pad to be stapled under the thickness gauge (7-7), then turn the handwheel clockwise to lower the feeler gauge and conversely, and counter-clockwise to raise the gauge (7-8). When properly adjusted, the gauge will be in firm contact with the stock to be stapled.

Most power stitchers have a foot lever release (7-9) for forming, driving, and clinching the staple. Only a quick, light pressure is used. If the release lever is held down, staples will come from the machine continuously. Make two staples with the machine before the stock is stapled, in order to clear the machine of staples previously cut at the former setting.

Two sizes of wire are usually kept in stock for stitching machines. No.

7-8. Adjust with handwheel

7-9. Foot trip on stitcher

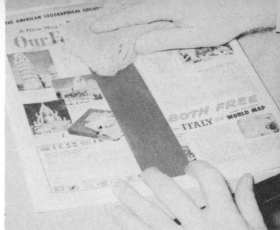

7-12. Moisten gummed Holland

7-10. Side stitching

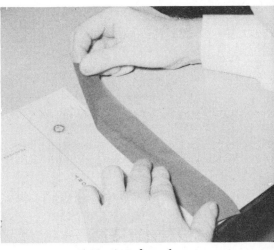

7-13. Attach to front cover

25 gauge is recommended for stapling thicknesses up to ¼ inch; 20 x 25 flat wire is recommended for most jobs over ¼ inch in thickness.

Stitchers may be set for either saddle stitching or side stitching. In sad-

7-11. Mark location on front cover

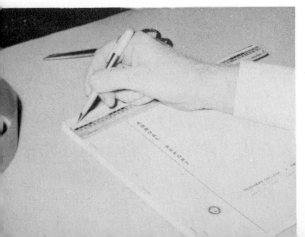

dle stitching, the staple is placed through the back of the booklet. See 7-6, page 81.

Thicker booklets are usually side stitched. Adjustable guides on the stitcher table are set to properly position the staple.

Gummed Holland, a cloth tape, is frequently used to cover the staples and the back of the book.

Mark the position of the gummed Holland on the front cover (7-11). Moisten the Holland with a sponge.

Attach moistened gummed Holland to the front of the book (7-13); then flip the book over, stretching the Holland around the back of the book.

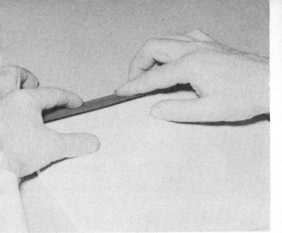

7-14. Stretch around to back

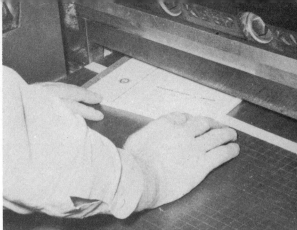

7-16. Trim booklet

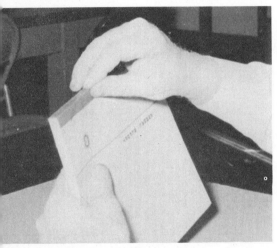

7-15. Define edges

7-17. Fold sheets of paper

Define the corner edges covered with Holland by sliding the thumb and index finger back and forth on each edge several times (7-15). After the Holland has been applied, the book is trimmed (7-16).

To fold, bring the two top corners of the sheet together and crease the paper (7-17).

One folded sheet inserted into another makes an eight-page signature (7-18). Five folded sheets assem-

Signature Binding

Signature binding is a term used to describe the binding of books made up of signatures. A signature is one or more sheets of paper folded together and assembled into one unit. For purposes of illustration, the binding of a book is started here with small sheets of paper that take a single fold each.

7-18. Assemble folded sheets into signatures

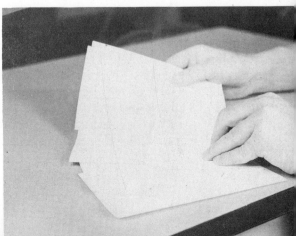

7-19. Jog assembled signatures to top and back

7-21. Clamp signatures in vise

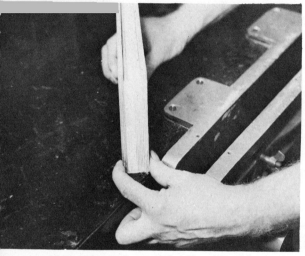

7-20. Plywood on each side of book

7-22. Mark saw kerfs with square

bled together make a twenty-page signature.

Assembled signatures are jogged to the top and back so they are even and straight (7-19).

Place a piece of ¼ inch plywood on each side of the assembled signatures and jog this assembly to top and back (7-20).

Hold plywood tightly to the signatures with the left hand, inserting it into the vise so the back protrudes about ½ inch above the vise jaws (7-21). Tighten the vise.

Make a mark ½ inch from the top and ½ inch from the bottom of the book at the back. Divide the length of the back into three parts and mark. This will provide four marks on the back of the book. Use a square to scribe lines at each of these points.

Using a back saw, make saw kerfs just deep enough to cut through the inner part of each signature (7-23). For twenty-page signatures, this will be about ¹⁄₁₆″ in depth.

The two saw kerfs near the top and bottom of the book are for the kettle stitch, and the two inner kerfs are used to provide an opening for the needle in sewing around soft twine cords.

84

7-23. Make saw kerfs with back saw

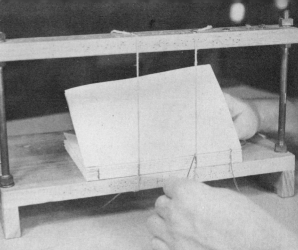

7-24. The sewing frame

Stretch soft twine between the base of the sewing frame and the beam above. Cords may be anchored at the top and bottom with thumbtacks (7-24).

The last signature of the book is placed on the base of sewing frame with the folded portion to the cords. Thread the needle, and start sewing from the bottom kettle-stitch kerf. Start the needle from the back of the signature, follow the fold inside the signature to the first cord, bringing the thread out and around the cord and back into the inside of the signature. Follow the fold, sew around the second cord into the signature, and bring the needle out of the top kettle-stitch kerf (7-25).

7-25. Sew signatures together

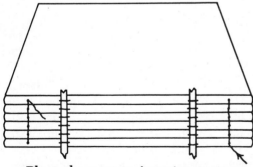

Place the next to last signature on top of the previous signature, being careful to keep the head of each sig-

nature to the same end each time. Insert the needle directly into the second signature and proceed in the same manner, which will return the needle to the bottom of the second signature. At this point, tie the thread so that the first two signatures are tied together at the kettle-stitch kerf on the bottom of the signature.

Place the third signature to be sewed in position. The needle goes directly into the third signature through the bottom kettle-stitch kerf. Sew the third signature in the same manner as the first two, bringing the needle out of the top kerf of the third signature.

From this point on, the kettle stitch is used to anchor the signatures together at both the top and the bottom. The kettle stitch is simply bringing the needle between the previous two signatures, catching the thread at the kettle-stitch kerf, and bringing the needle back through the loop before entering the next signature.

7-26. The kettle stitch

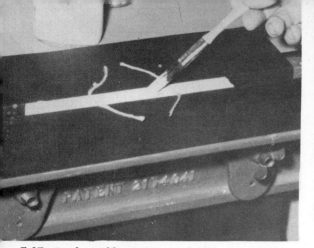

7-27. Apply padding compound to back of book

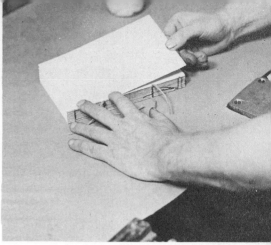

7-29. Attach end papers to book

Additional signatures are sewed into place in the same manner. When the last signature is sewed, cut the thread after the kettle stitch, leaving a tail of at least one inch.

Beginners tend to make the kettle stitch too tight and the thread around the cords too loose. Do not make the kettle stitch tighter than you are able to press the signatures together at the cords.

Two cords are sufficient for books up to 10 inches. Oves 10 inches, three cords are recommended.

The book may now be removed from the sewing frame. Trim the cords so they protrude beyond the back of the book approximately 1½ inches.

Line each side of vise with paper; clamp the book in the vise so the back of the book is square and even with

7-28. Apply paste to endpapers

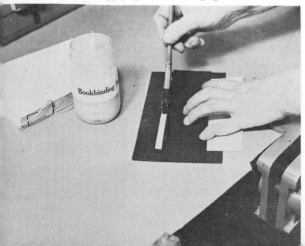

the top of the vise jaws. Apply one very thin coat of white padding compound to the back of the book (7-27). Be careful not to get padding compound on the parts of the soft twine cords that protrude over the edges of the book.

Open the cover on your textbook. You will notice a sheet of paper that is pasted to the inside of the cover and is attached to the first page of the book by a band of paste near the fold. This is called the endpaper or endsheet.

Fold two single sheets of endpaper, so that when folded, each is the same size as your book. Apply a band of paste about ¼ inch wide next to the fold. This is made even by placing a sheet of paper stock on the endpaper, exposing only the band to be pasted (7-28).

Attach endpapers to the back and front of the book, with the fold of the endpaper being even or flush with the back of the book (7-29).

Set the paper cutter to trim ⅛″ from the fore (outer) edge of the book (7-30). Then trim a like amount from the bottom edge. Trim the top last.

To round the back of the book, lay the book on a flat clean surface. Place one thumb under the pages at about

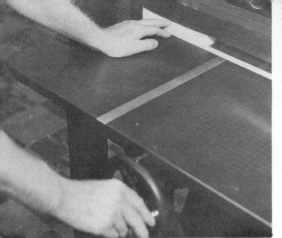

7-30. Trim three edges of book

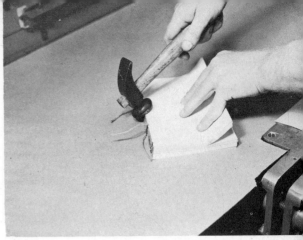

7-31. Round the book

the center of the book, spreading the four fingers across the endpaper. Lift this half of the book up about 2 inches; then squeeze the pages between thumb and fingers tightly. Gradually close the book as the back edge is struck lightly with the backing hammer across the entire length of the book (7-31). Repeat this procedure for the other half of the book. On books about ½ inch thick, this rounding should not exceed ⅛ of an inch. A book that has been sewed to a uniform tightness at the kettle stitch and around the cords will round more easily and be more uniform than a book that has not been sewed evenly.

Insert backing boards into vise and clamp book between the boards so the back of the book protrudes above the backing boards about ³/₁₆ of an inch. It is important that the amount protruding be uniform on both edges. With a backing hammer, strike the back of the book glancing blows, from the center to the outer edges, along the entire length on both edges (7-32). This operation forces the edges of the book over the edge of the backing board. Tap the soft twine cords into the back of the book as much as possible without damaging the back.

The amount of overhang, after the

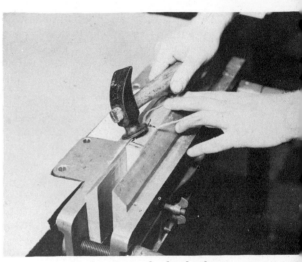

7-32. Back the book

book has been backed, should approximately equal the thickness of the binders board which will be used for the casing (7-33).

7-33. Appearance of book after backing

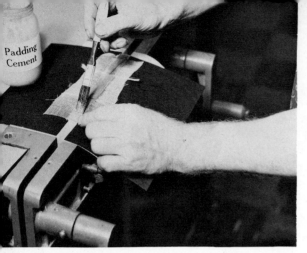

7-34. Attach super and head bands

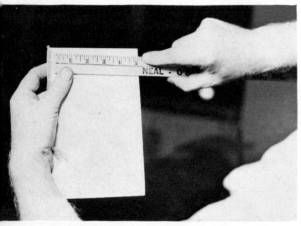

7-35. Measure book for casing

Remove book from the vise and examine the backing. If it is not complete or uniform, return it to the vise for additional work. When backing has been completed, line the vise with scrap paper and clamp the book so that just the back protrudes above

7-36. Cut binders board

the vise jaws. Cut a piece of super to a size that will be about ½ inch shorter than the length of the book and of a width that will extend over the edges of the book about 1½ inches. Cut two headbands about ¼ inch longer than the width of the book. After applying a coat of padding cement to the back, attach the super, approximately at the center to the book. The headbands are then attached, with rolled edges extending over the ends of the book (7-34). After the padding cement has dried, apply a second coat on top of the super and headbands and attach to this a strip of soft thin paper the same size as the back of the book. When this has dried (which will take about thirty minutes), trim the headbands with scissors so they are the same length as the width of the back, allowing for the curve.

The casing of a book is the outer covering, usually made from binders board and bookcloth. To find the width of board required, measure the distance from the back of the book to the fore edge, less an allowance at the back edge for the hinge, equal to the thickness of the binders board. At the fore edge of the book, add an amount equal to the overhang of the casing beyond the edge of the book. One eighth of an inch is satisfactory for most books. As shown in illustration 7-35, 5⅛ inches would be the correct width. To find the length of binders board needed, measure the length of the book and add the amount of overhang desired. If ⅛ inch overhang was established, ¼ inch is added to this measurement.

Cut binders board for both the front and back covers exactly the same size. A sheet-metal shear may be used if regular equipment is not available (7-36).

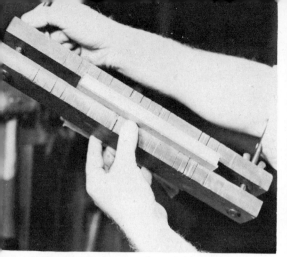

7-37. Clamp binders board to book

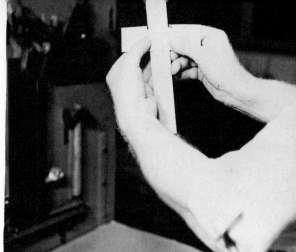

7-39. Check filler piece for cutting

Position the binders board on the front and the back of the book. Check carefully to see that the overhang is uniform. Place this assembly in a hand clamp such as illustrated in 7-37.

Cut a strip of paper about 1 inch wide and form it to the back of the book. Be sure to work the strip into the grooves on both front and back hinges. Mark this strip at the edge of the binders board on both front and back (7-38).

Cut a scrap piece of binders board the same width as the distance around the back of the book between the front and back binders board. Check this with the original measuring strip (7-39).

Lay the bookcloth on a flat surface with the back side up. Front and back

7-40. Measure the bookcloth for cutting

boards, separated by the filler strip, are then placed on the bookcloth, which is cut to a size that will permit a fold-over of about ¾ inch on all sides (7-40).

38. Locate bend of strip at front and back

7-41. Position binders board on bookcloth

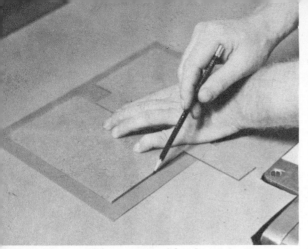

7-42. Mark position of binders board

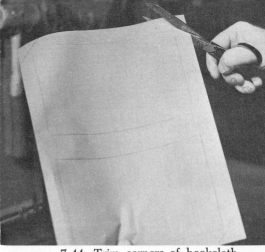

7-44. Trim corners of bookcloth

After the bookcloth has been marked and cut to size, the front and back covers, separated by the filler strip, are positioned on the back of the bookcloth. *It is very important to align the two pieces of binders board with a straightedge* (7-41).

The position of the front and back binders board is outlined with pencil on the back of the bookcloth (7-42).

At a 45° angle, place a mark on the bookcloth about ¼ inch from each corner (7-43).

Trim the four corners of the bookcloth with scissors (7-44). This is essential to make a nicked corner.

Lay several sheets of clean newspaper on a flat surface in preparation for applying paste to the bookcloth. Hold the bookcloth firmly with one hand; then work the paste into the

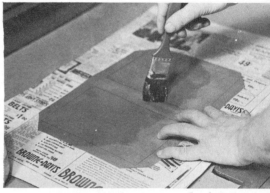

7-45. Apply paste to bookcloth

cloth with a brush (7-45). *Do not leave lumps of paste.*

When paste has been applied to about half of the cloth, pull away the top sheet of newsprint that has paste on it from the brush going over the edge of the cloth (7-46). Turn the

7-43. Mark bookcloth for nicked corner

7-46. Keep bookcloth on clean surface

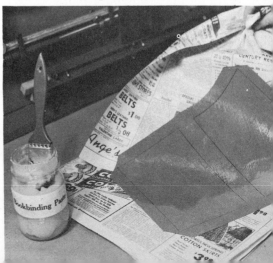

7-47. Locate boards and back lining

7-48. Fold bookcloth over top and bottom

on the binders board; then stretch the cloth over the edges as tightly as possible (7-48). Do not allow the binders board to slip on the bookcloth in this operation.

In making the nicked corner, crease the cover cloth around both corners, which will pull up a small triangle of bookcloth which should be folded in when the bookcloth is folded over the edge (7-49).

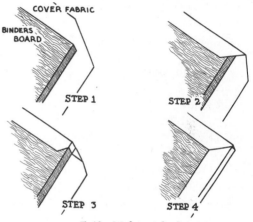

7-49. Make nicked corner

bookcloth around and apply paste to the other half. Remove another sheet of newspaper so the bookcloth will again be on a clean surface.

Position the front and back covers as previously marked in pencil (7-47). If there is any question as to proper location, the binders board filler strip may be placed between the front and back cover to double-check proper location. Likewise, a straight-edge is used to double-check alignment of the front and back covers. A strip of lining paper is then cut to the same size as the back of the book. Position this in the center between the front and back covers.

Carefully fold over the bookcloth at the top and bottom of the casing. Press down with the heel of the hands

When the corners have been made, the bookcloth on the fore edges is folded over and stretched in the same manner as the top and bottom edges (7-50).

While the paste is still soft, define the edges by pressing each edge be-

7-50. Stretch bookcloth

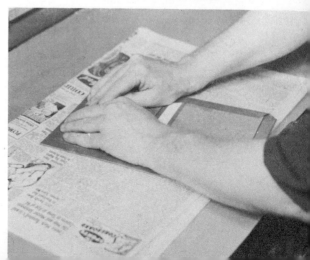

7-51. Define edges on casing

7-52. Press the casing

tween the thumb and index finger (7-51).

Place a piece of wax paper on each side of the casing, and slide it into the book press (7-52). This should be left in the press under pressure until it is thoroughly dry, usually for about twenty-four hours. Additional casings may be pressed at the same time if a sheet of pressed board, smooth on both sides, is interleaved between casings.

There are several ways the casing may be printed. Hot stamping is frequently used in commercial plants as well as in school work centers (7-53). The casing may be printed by letterpress, or the silk screen process may be used. It is recommended that the casing be printed after it has been dried under pressure.

While the casing is drying, separate and fan out the soft twine cords which extend beyond the back edges of the book (7-54). The twine is easily untwisted and the fibers separated. The fibers are separated so that they will be less noticeable when covered by the endpapers. Do not be alarmed if it appears that parts of the fibers break from the cord. This is to be expected.

"Hanging a book" is a trade term which refers to securing the inside of the book to the casing. Before the inside of the book is pasted in, fit the casing to the book to make sure that it is the proper size (7-55). Crease the bookcloth at the hinges and around the back, so the shape of the casing conforms to the shape of the book. When the casing has been fitted, lay the book on a flat surface in preparation for pasting. Be careful

7-53. Print on casing

7-54. Separate fibers of cord

7-55. Fit casing to book

7-56. Apply paste to end paper

not to shift the position of the book in relation to the casing.

Lift the cover from the book, interleave a sheet of newspaper under the exposed endpaper, then apply a coat of paste to the entire endpaper (7-56). The frayed ends of the cords and the super are also pasted down to the endsheet. *Do not apply paste to the back of the book.* While the paste is being brushed and worked into the super with one hand, hold the book with the other hand to keep it from slipping. The newspaper inserted under the endsheet to catch the excess paste is now removed. Hold the book with the left hand and bring the cover into position with one hand, making the first contact with the pasted endpaper at the hinge. The cover on the other side is pasted in the same manner.

After completing the pasting operation, examine the endpapers to make sure there are no wrinkles before the book is pressed.

Press boards are usually made of plywood with a brass strip along one edge. Interleave a clean sheet of wax paper between each of the newly pasted endsheets. Locate the book between two press boards, placing the brass strip in the hinge of each cover. Put this assembly under pressure in the standing press until thoroughly dry (7-57). This takes several hours, so leave the assembly in the press overnight.

When the book comes from the standing press, remove the wax paper and clean up around the edges of the front and back endpapers, if excess paste was squeezed out in the standing press (7-58).

7-57. Position press boards on book

7-58. Completed book

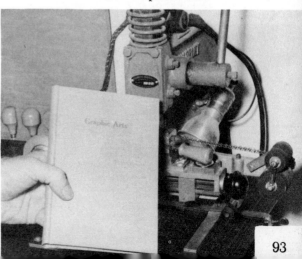

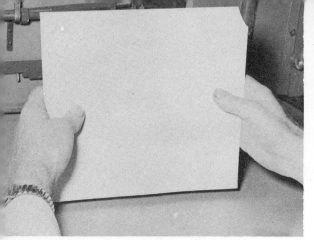

7-59. Jog loose sheets to top and back

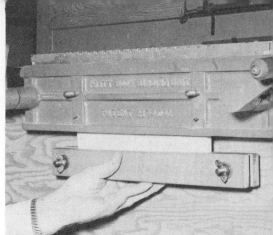

7-60. Clamp jogged sheets in drill jig of v

Loose Sheet Binding

Loose sheet binding is a term which describes the binding together of sheets of paper which have not been folded and assembled into signatures. This type of binding differs from signature binding both in the method of sewing and the procedure in making the case.

Place a blank sheet of paper at the back and front of the book. The sheets to be bound are jogged together at the top and back of the book (7-59). When all sheets are even, place a hand clamp at the fore edge of the book, which will make it easier to clamp the book into the vise for drilling. Attach the drill jig to the vise.

Insert the book into the vise from the bottom; then clamp it into position so the back of the book is even with the top of the drill jig (7-60).

Adjust the book laterally in the drill jig so the holes at the top and at the bottom of the book will be equidistant from the ends. Drill the end holes not less than ½ inch from the top and bottom.

Drill $\frac{1}{16}''$ holes through the side of the book, using an ordinary hand drill (7-61). Do not force the drill, push very lightly, and keep the drill turning freely. Make a hole at each point provided by the drill jig.

Irish linen thread No. 20/2h in a single strand is recommended for sewing loose sheets together. Estimate length of thread needed to sew over and back from each side of the book. Start the needle through either the top or bottom hole and pull the thread through the first hole, leaving about 3 inches of thread protruding from the book (7-62).

Pass the needle through the drilled

7-61. Drill holes through side of book

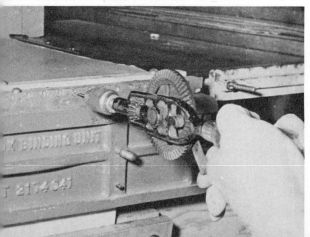

7-62. Sew through side of book

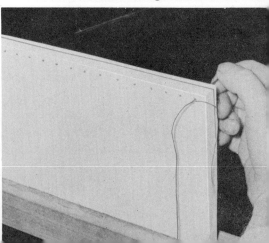

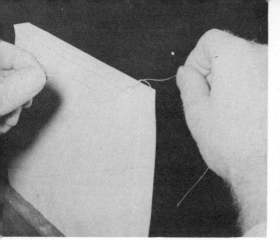

7-63. Tie two ends of thread together

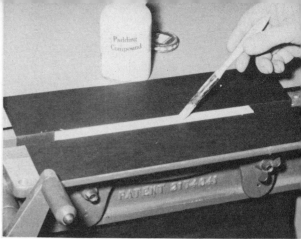

7-64. Apply padding compound to back of book

holes all the way up and then back again, until the needle is returned to the starting point. The two ends of the thread will now be directly opposite one another on each side of the book; tie these ends together (7-63).

Remove the drill jig from the vise; then line the jaws on each side with a folded sheet of newspaper. Clamp the book in the vise so the back is even with the top of the vise jaws. Apply a thin coat of white padding cement to the back, to assist in making the book more rigid and easier to handle in succeeding operations (7-64).

Remove the blank sheets of paper from the front and the back of the book. Attach endpapers to both front and back, using the same procedure as illustrated in signature binding (7-29).

After endsheets have been at-

tached, trim three edges of the book (7-66). The fore edge is trimmed first, then the bottom, and the top is last. The amount of trim will vary with different books. As a general rule, ⅛" is considered a minimum amount that can be trimmed from each edge.

Super, head bands, and backing strip may now be attached (7-67). The procedure is the same as illustrated in signature binding (7-34).

Case making for loose sheet binding is considerably easier than for signature binding. Front and back covers are cut to the same size. For a ⅛" overhang, the width of the binders board is the same as the width of the book from the back to the fore edge. The length of the binders board is ¼" greater than the distance from the top to the bottom of the book. A third piece of binders

7-65. Attach end papers to back of book

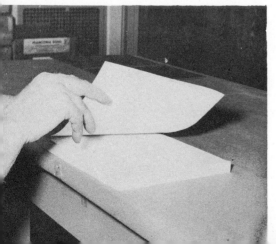

7-66. Trim three edges

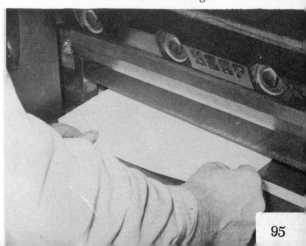

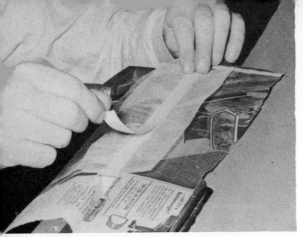

7-67. Attach super, head bands, and backing strip

7-70. Apply paste to bookcloth

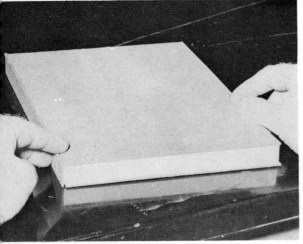

7-68. Cut binders board

board for the covers and the binders board for the back of the book is $\frac{5}{16}''$. Two strips of wood cut to $\frac{5}{16}''$ square work very well as spacers to assure parallel alignment. With the binders board and spacers in position, measure the bookcloth, to extend $\frac{3}{4}''$ beyond the binders board on all four sides (7-69). The size of the bookcloth and the location of the binders board are marked in pencil on the back side of the bookcloth. Cut the bookcloth to size.

Apply paste to the bookcloth (7-70) in the same manner as for signature binding (7-55).

In signature binding, the making of a nicked corner was described. Since the library corner is also commonly used, this procedure is described for loose sheet binding only for purposes of illustration. Either type of corner might be used in making a casing.

To make a library corner, position

board for the back of the book is cut to the same length as the covers, and the width equals the thickness of the book plus the top and bottom covers (7-68).

The space between the binders

7-69. Lay out binders board on bookcloth

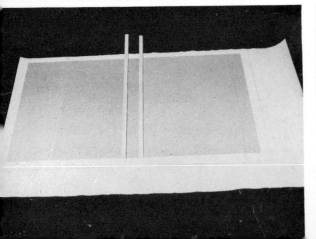

7-71. Fold corner of bookcloth at 45° angle

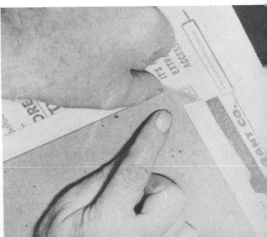

7-72. Stretch bookcloth over edges

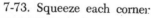
7-74. Dry casing under pressure

the binders board on the pasted book-cloth. Pull the corner of the bookcloth over the corner of the binders board at a 45° angle (7-71). Apply a small amount of paste to the folded portion which extends beyond the binders board.

Crease the bookcloth over the edge of the binders board at the corners; then stretch the bookcloth over the edge tightly and press firmly (7-72).

The library corner tends to be more bulky than the nicked corner, and for this reason it is recommended that each corner be squeezed separately in the standing press (7-73). The additional pressure will make a neater appearing corner.

Place a sheet of wax paper on each side of the casing, which then is dried between smooth surfaces under pressure (7-74).

When the casing is thoroughly dry,

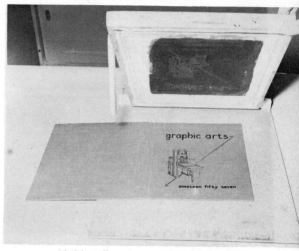
7-75. Silk screen printing on cover

the cover may be printed, hot stamped, or silk screened (7-75).

The procedure for hanging a loose-sheet bound book (7-77), is the same as the procedure used to hang a signature bound book. See illustration 7-55.

7-73. Squeeze each corner

7-76. Hang book in casing

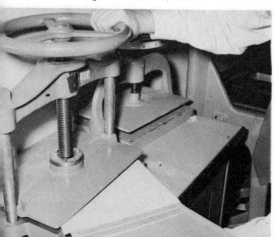

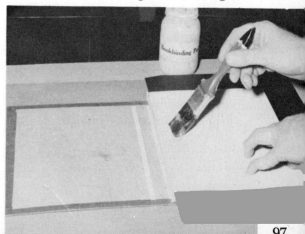

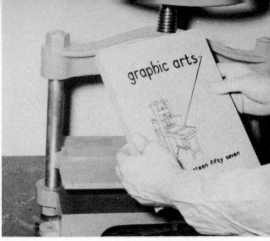

7-77. Dry book between pressing boards under pressure

7-78. Completed book

When the book has dried under pressure, remove it from the press and clean up excess paste which may have been squeezed from the endsheets (7-78).

Marbling Paper

The endpapers, or endsheets, of a book are frequently decorated with various colors to give a marbled effect.

Early in the seventeenth century marbled paper was first made in Europe. In about the middle of the century, Dutch marbled paper was exported to England, wrapped around toys and thus passed duty free. When the parcels were unwrapped, the marbled paper was carefully pressed and sold to English bookbinders. They used it for endpapers in some of their finest bindings. Upon close examination, it is apparent that the endpapers had been crushed and wrinkled before being used for this purpose.

There never has been much marbling done in America, and at the present time the art has almost entirely passed out of the picture. American bookbinders have depended almost entirely upon imported, handmade marbleized paper, although American publishers frequently use lithographed paper which resembles original hand marbleized sheets.

Yet the process of marbleizing paper is quite simple. Artistic success depends upon the skill of the individual doing the work. Various techniques and procedures in the practice of the art have been developed, especially in the preparation of the ink and the solution upon which the pigment is floated.

A limited amount of marbling is done at the federal printing office. But the process requires ingredients not available to the average school.

A simplified method, satisfactory for making a limited number of marbleized sheets, can be accomplished with materials available in most school work centers.

Effective patterns can be made by thinning regular printers ink with a solvent such as turpentine or a standard ink reducer (7-79). The ink is

7-79. Thin printers ink with solvent

7-80. Fill shallow tray with water

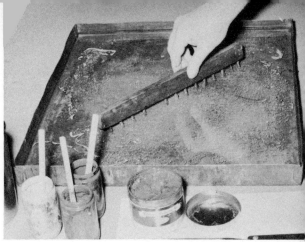

7-82. Comb pattern

thoroughly dissolved to the consistency of water, using a separate container for each color.

Place about an inch of water in a shallow tray (7-80). The thinned ink is then dropped onto the surface of the water with a small paintbrush (7-81). Different color schemes and predominent colors will depend upon the color of inks used and the amount of each color placed upon the surface of the water.

Draw a simple comb over the surface of the water in two directions to form a pattern (7-82). Such a comb can be made by driving a row of small finishing nails into a piece of wood.

The sheet of paper is then placed in contact with the surface containing the colored pattern, which is transferred to the paper (7-83). Before making another sheet, the inking

7-83. Touch paper to surface

and combing operations must be repeated. The surface of the water may be cleaned by drawing a paper towel over it. This picks up the ink remaining on the water.

7-81. Drop ink onto surface

7-84. Iron the marbleized sheets

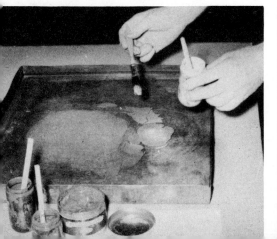

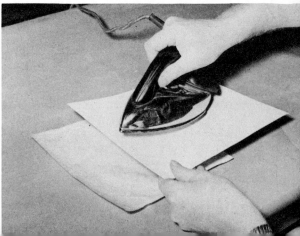

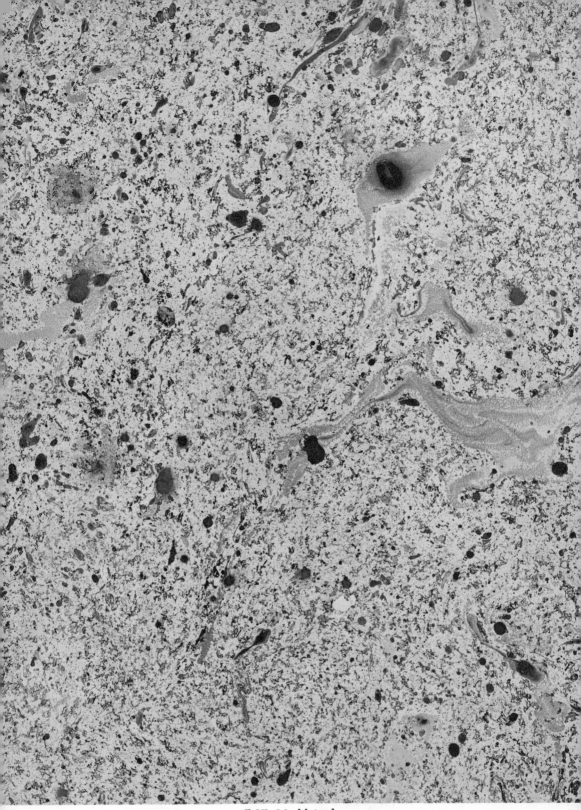

7-85. Marbleized paper

When the marbled sheets have been removed from the bath, the paper as well as the ink will be wet. Place the marbled sheets on a layer of newspaper to dry.

With an ordinary clothes iron, wrinkles caused by the water can be removed. Lay the marbleized sheet on paper, place another plain sheet of paper over it, and press with the iron.

Sample Tests—Chapter 7

Completion

Example: 1. Books are bound in order to __preserve__ them.

1. Padding compound is applied with a brush, working from the _____ of the pile to the _____ _____.

2. Endpapers should be attached to a book before the book is _____.

3. A _____ is one or more sheets of paper folded or assembled into one unit.

4. A _____ _____ is used to hold the cords in a vertical position while sewing a signature together.

5. A band of paste about _____ inch wide is recommended for attaching the end paper to the book.

Multiple Choice

Example: a   1. Bookcloth is used (a) to cover binders board (b) to hold the book in the casing (c) to make head bands.

_____ 6. Super is attached to the (a) fore edge of the book (b) top of the book (c) back of the book.

_____ 7. Head bands are attached to the book (a) after the book has been rounded (b) after the book has been trimmed (c) just before the book has been trimmed.

_____ 8. Loose sheet binding differs from signature binding in (a) method of sewing (b) method of making the case (c) both method of sewing and case making.

Matching

Example: a   1. Thread   a. Needle

_____11. Folded sheets   a. Drill jig

_____12. Stitching   b. Casing

_____13. Loose sheets   c. Signature

_____14. Bookcloth   d. Cords

_____15. Separate fibers   e. Wire

True-False

Example: Ⓣ F 1. Pads should be trimmed on three exposed edges.

T F 16. In signature binding, sewing should be done before the book is trimmed.

T F 17. In bookbinding, super and head bands have the same function.

T F 18. Binders board should be cut to size before the bookcloth is cut.

T F 19. The library corner is adaptable to any type of case.

T F 20. Extensive marbling is still being done in the United States.

_____ 9. The kettle stitch is used in (a) signature binding (b) loose sheet binding (c) both signature and loose sheet binding.

_____10. Marbling was first done in Europe in (a) 13th Century (b) 17th Century (c) 19th Century.

Chapter 8

PLANOGRAPHIC PRINTING

PLANOGRAPHIC printing is done with a plate on which the printing and the non-printing areas are on the same plane or level. Lithography is a planographic process.

Alois Senefelder, a Bavarian, accidentally discovered the lithographic principle in 1798 while he was experimenting with transfering designs to a stone surface from which he made stone relief plates.

During these experiments he softened the paper with its previously prepared gum arabic surface by dipping it in water before laying it face down on the stone for transfering the design from the paper to the stone by pressure. Peeling the paper from the stone, the transferred design appeared in reverse on the stone as desired. (Later, proofs of type were also transferred in this manner.) Senefelder noticed that if a few drops of oil were on the water, the oil would distribute itself evenly over those areas of the stone bearing the inked design, but would not adhere to the un-inked portion. This fact led him to further experiments on cleanly polished limestone. He inscribed a stone with a piece of his greasy "resist" crayon, poured thin gum arabic solution over it, and then rubbed the whole surface of the stone with a sponge containing ink. All the places marked with the greasy crayon took the ink and the remainder of the stone surface, being wet, did not. Senefelder found that he could transfer as many impressions as he pleased to paper by repeating the gumming and inking operations. Here was a printing process, depending solely upon chemical action, that was fundamentally different from all others.

Since lithography was discovered, improvements have become commonplace. Zinc plates with a rough or "grained" surface gradually replaced smooth stones. It became possible to transfer designs photographically to the printing plate. Later developments provided aluminum plates, as well as plastic and paper plates.

There are several basic terms in connection with planographic printing which should be understood. Lithographic printing refers to printing directly from a lithographic plate to a printing surface. Offset lithography refers to the method of printing from the lithographic plate to a rubber blanket, then transferring the design from the rubber blanket to the printing surface. Photo-offset lithography refers to making the lithographic plate with a photographic process, then printing the plate with the offset method. "Web-fed" or "Roto" refers to feeding the paper into the press from a roll of paper, rather than from a pile of single sheets.

There are single color and multi-color presses. A single color press is designed to print one color from a single plate at one time. A multi-color press is essentially two or more single color printing units in tandem. A four color press has four printing units in tandem. A plate is attached to the cylinder of each printing unit. The paper automatically moves from one unit to the next. In this way, the yellow plate might be printed in the first unit, the red plate in the second unit, the blue plate in the third unit, and the black plate in the fourth unit. Four or more colors can also be printed on a single color press; however, the stock must be printed in four separate operations.

As an introduction to this important phase of the graphic arts, the procedure in making direct image plates, photographic plates, and the printing of these plates will be discussed. A model 1250 Multilith will illustrate the printing process. Other very excellent presses, such as the A. B. Dick and Davidson machines, are similar and may be operated according to manufacturers' directions.

Direct Image Plates

Direct image plates may be made of zinc, aluminum, plastic, or paper. The same general procedure is used is making each.

Special typewriter ribbons are made for typing on direct image paper plates (8-1). It is recommended that copy be typewritten on paper first to make sure proper margins and spacing are established. The plates are marked on the surface, indicating the proper position of the paper in relation to the plate. When several pages with like margins are to be printed, it is desirable to maintain the same margins when the plates are typed. This reduces the number of

8-1. Typing on paper plate

changes required when the plate is printed on the press.

A soft eraser is used to erase errors in typing. This must be done carefully so the surface on the plate is not destroyed. It is not essential that all traces of the typed letter or letters are removed.

The plate must be handled carefully. Keep it clean, for dirty finger marks will reproduce. Do not fold or bend the plate to a point where the surface is cracked. A crack in the surface will print.

Lithographic pencils may be used to write or draw on the plate. Place a clean piece of paper under the hand when writing or drawing on a plate.

Photographic Plates

Photographic plates are made from negatives. Copy made up of lines is reproduced from a line negative. Photographs are reproduced from halftone negatives. A line negative is made by photographing the copy with a regular copying camera. Halftone negatives are made by photographing the original photo or shaded drawing through a screen. The screen is a series of opaque lines either imposed on a transparent plastic sheet or a piece of glass. The number of lines per inch determines the fineness

8-2. Negative and masking paper

8-3. Place mask over negative

or coarseness of the screen. For lithographic printing, the screen may vary from 120 lines to 150 lines per square inch. If a halftone negative is examined under a magnifying glass, it is evident that the negative is made up of a series of dots. In light areas, the dots are smaller and further apart than in the darker areas. This screening of the negative makes it possible to reproduce the various tones in the photograph from very light to very dark.

Mount the negative or negatives on a sheet of opaque paper just slightly larger than the plate (8-2). This is called a "flat." Commercial masking paper with horizontal and vertical guide lines is available to make it easier to locate the negative accurately and squarely on the mask.

The negatives are placed right side up on a light table and positioned

under the mask in the proper relationship to each other and in the proper position (8-3).

With a small piece of tape, the corners of the negative are attached to the back of the masking paper (8-4). Place the piece of tape as far away from the image area as possible. Since this is a temporary holding device, only the corners are fastened.

When the negative has been secured to the back of the opaque paper, use a sharp knife to cut out the mask in all areas which are to be printed (8-5).

Attach the edges of the mask to the negative with opaque tape (8-6). This is done on the top side of the "flat." There is no objection to placing the tape close to a printing area on this side of the mask.

Negatives frequently have small pin holes in non-printing areas. These

8-4. Tape corners of negative to mask

8-5. Cut mask from image area

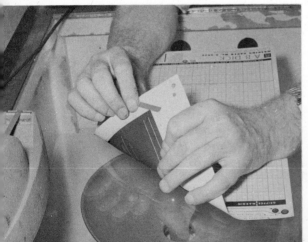

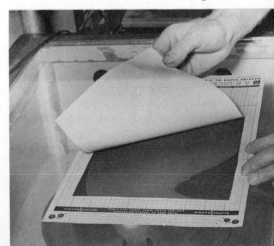

8-6. Tape mask to negative

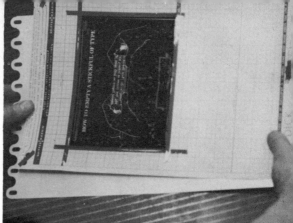

8-8. Locate flat over plate

are visible on the light table. Use a fine brush to apply photographers opaque to cover these holes (8-7). It is advisable to thin the photographers opaque with water. The photographers opaque should be applied to the "top side" of the negative; this is opposite the emulsion side, so if an error is made, the opaque may easily be removed with a damp cloth.

Pre-sensitized 3-M brand plates are exposed on the side bearing the trademark imprint. Place the flat squarely over the plate and locate the plate together with the flat in the exposure frame (8-8).

Expose the plate for seven minutes. The light passes through the transparent areas of the negative (8-9). The light-sensitive emulsion on the plate is hardened where struck by the light, but remains soft in the opaque areas not exposed to the light. Re-

8-9. Exposing plate

move the plate from the exposure frame, placing it on a work surface with the image side upward.

Pour a puddle of process gum on the plate, spreading it evenly over the entire plate with a clean sponge and

8-7. Opaquing negative

8-10. Coat plate with gum

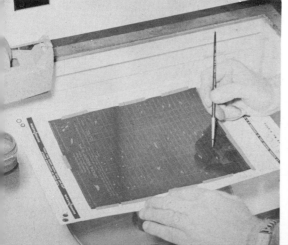

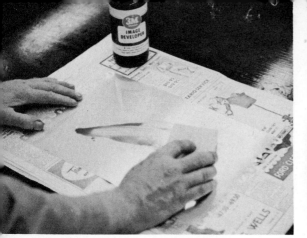

8-11. Pour developing ink on plate

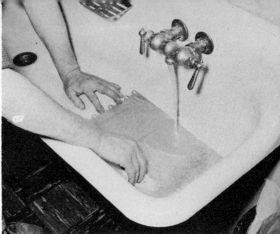

8-12. Wash out plate

scrubbing away the unhardened emulsion (8-10).

Before the gum dries, pour a puddle of developing ink about the size of a nickel on the plate (8-11). With a sponge, dampened with water, spread the developing ink over the image area of the plate. Use a light pressure. The image will then become visible. For best results, it should be a uniform, cherry red.

Run cold water over the image surface of the plate, swabbing it lightly with a clean piece of cotton (8-12). Wash away all traces of the developing ink in the non-image area.

Place the plate on layers of newspapers, which will absorb the moisture from the back side. Moisten a clean cotton pad with process gum and spread this over the entire plate on the image side (8-13). The purpose of coating the plate with gum is to provide a protective covering which will keep the plate clean.

Small Offset Press Operation

The principle of lithographic offset press operation is the same for both small and large presses. All presses have dampening, inking, printing, feeding, and delivery mechanisms which are generally similar although they vary in detail.

The order of procedure in preparing a press for operation might not be in the exact sequence as presented here. However, unless there is good reason for changing this sequence, it is recommended that it be followed in order to establish a systematic method which will be easier to remember.

The Dampening System

Under numerous trade-names, fountain concentrates are available

8-13. Gum plate

8-14. Mix fountain solution

8-15. Place fountain solution container on press

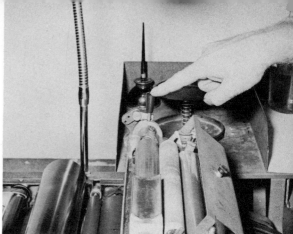

8-16. Ratchet control for fountain solution

which are mixed with distilled water and used to dampen the plate. Follow the manufacturer's recommendations in mixing this solution (8-14). Grasp the plastic top of the fountain solution bottle firmly, being careful not to exert pressure on the outlet from the cap. Unscrew the bottle, wash it, put in the fountain concentrate, then fill the bottle with distilled water. Not all mixed fountain solutions will keep for long periods, so do not mix large quantities at one time.

Hold the fountain solution container in a horizontal position, with the outlet downward. Locate the container on the press. Be sure the outlet is seated (8-15).

There is a ratchet control on the dampening fountain roller which is used to regulate the amount this roller is turned, and makes it possible to regulate the amount of moisture

fed into the dampening system (8-16). Normal setting of the lever is a vertical position. To the right of vertical position reduces moisture flow, to the left of vertical increases moisture flow.

Moisture is transferred from the fountain roller to an oscillating intermediate roller by a flannel cloth (molleton) covered ductor roller — the small roller next to the fountain roller. The metal oscillating roller transfers the moisture to a large molleton roller, which transfers the moisture to the plate (8-17).

The Inking Mechanism

When the press is not in operation, the various inking rollers should not be in contact with one another.

On the far side of the press from the operator is located the control lever which engages and disengages

8-17. Dampening system

8-18. Engage form rollers

8-19. Engage large distributor roller

8-22. Adjust ink fountain

8-20. Place ink in fountain

the form rollers from contact with the distribution rollers. When the control lever is in a vertical position, the rollers are disengaged. Engage the form rollers with the distribution rollers by turning the control lever to

8-21. Press handwheel

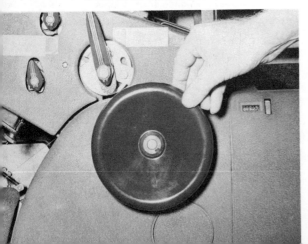

the right ¼ turn so it is pointing to the delivery end of the press (8-18). This lever is now left engaged until printing has been completed and the ink rollers of the press have been cleaned.

The large ink distribution roller on top of the press is held in position by a nicked support at each end. When the press is idle for a prolonged period, this roller should be held from contact with the other rollers by the nicked support against the frame of the press. Lower this roller so that it will be supported by the distribution rollers below it (8-19).

Skim dried ink from the top of the ink can, wrap it in paper, and place it in a metal waste container. Use an ink knife to place ink into the ink fountain (8-20). Then turn the roller counterclockwise with the handwheel on the operator's side of the press. Sufficient ink is placed in the fountain so the ink will roll as the fountain roller is turned.

The press may be turned over by hand in either direction with the press handwheel on the operator's side of the press (8-21). After ink has been placed in the fountain, turn the handwheel until the ductor roller is in firm contact with the ink fountain roller.

The small adjusting screws along the back of the ink fountain are used

8-23. Ink fountain ratchet control

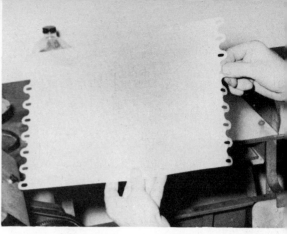

8-24. Bend down serrated edges of plate

to regulate the flow of ink from the ink fountain. When the thumbscrew is turned clockwise, the blade of the fountain is brought closer to the ink fountain roller, which reduces the flow of ink. Turning the thumbscrews counterclockwise has the opposite effect (8-22). Assuming that the plate to be printed will require uniform inking, the ink fountain is set to provide a uniform flow of ink across the entire surface.

Start with the center adjusting screw, working alternately on each side toward the outer edges of the fountain until a uniform flow of ink from the fountain has been established. In order to check the flow of ink while adjusting the fountain screws, the ductor roller must be in contact with the fountain roller, and the fountain roller must be turned continuously in a counterclockwise direction.

The ink fountain ratchet control (8-23) is "off" when moved to the extreme left. One notch to the right permits a slight movement of the fountain roller each time the press turns over.

There is enough ink on the ductor roller to ink the press, so set the ink ratchet control to the "off" position until the press is completely set up and ready for printing. With the

ratchet control in a vertical position, a medium stroke of the fountain roller is made. When the press run is started, adjust the ratchet control to provide the correct volume of ink for the particular job to be printed.

Plate Installation

In preparation for installing the plate on the press, hold the plate with the image side upward with one hand, and bend the serrated edges at the bottom of the plate downward (8-24).

Turn the press with the handwheel so the plate can be hooked on the pin bar of the plate cylinder (8-25).

Hook the top of the plate on the plate cylinder pin bar, holding it tightly with one hand at the bottom of the plate. With the other hand, turn the handwheel counterclockwise

8-25. Plate cylinder turned to position

109

8-26. Hook plate on pin bar

8-28. Tighten pin bar thumb screw

until only about 1½ inches of the plate is visible (8-26).

With one hand, hold the plate snug to the cylinder by pressing down on the plate. With the other hand, raise the pin bar and hook the plate to it (8-27).

Tighten the pin bar thumbscrew (8-28). Use only finger pressure to tighten the screw. Turn the press so the top of the plate is exposed, and crease the plate at the edge of the cylinder. Repeat this at the bottom of the plate. Tighten the thumbscrew again, and also the lock nut, so the thumbscrew will not loosen during operation of the press.

There are two switches located close together on the operator's side of the press. The one on the left operates the press; the one on the right operates the feeding mechanism. Turn on the press switch and idle the

8-29. Turn on press switch

press for about two minutes (8-29). This will distribute the ink and also distribute moisture in the dampening system.

Above and to the left of the feed

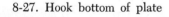

8-27. Hook bottom of plate

8-30. Lower feeder elevator

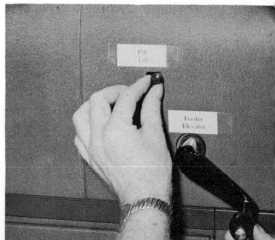

8-31. Adjust sheet detector

8-34. Move side guides on feed table

8-32. Place stock in feeder

elevator crank is the control lever for the pile lift. Push this lever to the right, in which position the feed elevator crank can be turned counterclockwise to lower the feeder elevator

8-33. Adjust back pile guides

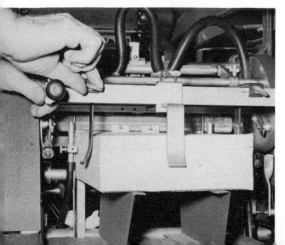

(8-30). Lower the elevator several inches to permit loading a small quantity of stock to be printed.

Fold a sheet of stock to be printed. With the press running, adjust the sheet detector by inserting the folded sheet under the feeler gauge (8-31). This is set so that one sheet will pass into the press; a double sheet won't.

Locate stock approximately in the center of the feeder. Adjust the front pile guides to the pile of stock. Allow about $\frac{1}{64}$ inch clearance between the stock and the front pile guides on each side (8-32). Raise the feeder elevator with the crank so the top of the pile is even with the front of the pile guide.

Push the stock forward so it is in firm contact with the front pile guides and is located squarely in the feeder. Bring the rear side pile guides to within $\frac{1}{64}$ inch of the stock pile on each side (8-33). Adjust the back guide so that it is in light contact with the pile. Push the control lever for the pile lift to the left. In this position the stock pile will be automatically raised to its proper working level.

Move both side guides on the feed table to the outer sides of the feed table so they will not interfere with the movement of the sheet to the press cylinder (8-34).

111

8-35. Remove gum from plate

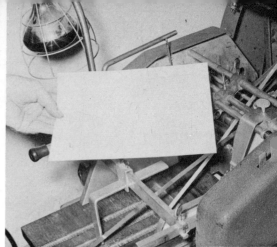

8-38. Examine printed copy

8-36. Etch the plate

Make First Impression

With a clean cotton pad, moistened with water, wipe the gum from the plate (8-35). It is advisable to start at either end of the plate, then go

8-37. Ink the plate

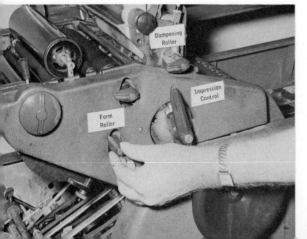

over the surface twice, to insure complete removal of the protective process gum coating.

Moisten a cotton pad with plate etch and go over the entire plate (8-36). This will desensitize and clean the plate.

Before the plate etch has an opportunity to dry, start the press, drop the dampening roller, and drop the two ink rollers. Let the press run for about thirty seconds (8-37). Watch the plate cylinder. If ink is picked up in the non-printing areas, it indicates insufficient moisture is being applied to the plate. Raise all rollers; then stop the press. Make another application of plate etch, start the press, drop the dampening roller, drop the two ink rollers, place the press on impression, and start the feeder, feeding about two sheets into the press. Raise all rollers, take the press off impression; then stop the press.

Examine the printed copy (8-38). The ink will be light because only a minimum amount has been distributed on the ink rollers. Compare head margin and side margins with the original copy.

Adjust Margins

Turn the press by hand until the scale on the right side of the plate

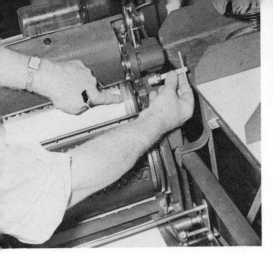

8-39. Adjust head margin

8-40. Wash blanket cylinder

cylinder is visible. In this position, a "T" wrench can be inserted through a hole in the press frame on the far side of the press opposite the scale on the plate cylinder (8-39). Loosen the hexagon head binding screw, leaving the wrench on the screw, holding it with one hand. With the other hand, turn the handwheel, which will move the mark on the plate cylinder in relation to the scale immediately to the right. To decrease head margins, move the mark on the plate cylinder downward in relation to the scale. Tighten the binding screw with the "T" wrench.

Moisten a wiping cloth with a solvent. Wash the blanket cylinder, turning the press with the handwheel (8-40). It is necessary to wash the blanket cylinder every time the head margin is changed.

The side guide on the operator's side of the feed table moves back and forth. Its function is to position the sheet for the side margin. The pile of paper is located in the magazine so that the sheet will miss the left guide on the feed table by about ¼ inch. The left side guide will then move the sheet about ⅛ inch. After this guide has been adjusted to provide the proper side margins, turn the press by hand until the guide has

8-41. Adjust side guides

moved to the operator's extreme right. In this position, place a sheet of stock to be printed on the feed table. Bring the right guide into contact with the sheet compressing the spring about ¹⁄₃₂ of an inch (8-41). After these adjustments have been made, start the press, then start the feeder, and again stop the press when the sheet is on the feedboard so it will be possible to check the relationship of the pile in the feeder with the side guide adjustments.

If necessary, move pile in magazine so sheet does not strike left side guide.

8-42. Adjust upper pull-out rolls

8-43. Adjust jogger

Adjust Delivery

Apply plate etch to the plate, start the press, drop the dampening roller, drop the ink rollers, place the press on impression, start the feeder, and feed two or three sheets, stopping the press before the last sheet is delivered (8-42). In this position, move the upper pull-out rollers to the margin of the sheet being printed. Turn the press by hand until the sheet touches the lower pull-out rollers. Locate these in the margin of the sheet.

With the sheet being held by the lower pull-out rollers, move the jogger wing close to the sheet on the operator's side (8-43). Turn the press by hand until the jogger wing on the far side of the press is moved toward the sheet as far as it will go. Move this wing so it contacts the sheet in this position. Set the stop to the end of the sheet.

Start Run

The press is now ready for operation. Set the counter (8-44). Set both ink and dampening fountain roller ratchet controls to a vertical position. Go over the plate with plate etch, start the press, drop the dampening roller, drop the ink rollers, place the press on impression, and start the feeder. After feeding several sheets,

raise all rollers, take the press off impression, then stop the press. Carefully examine the printed sheet. Check (1) location, (2) printing quality, and (3) inking. Assuming these points are satisfactory, the run may be started. It is advisable to *load the feeder* at this point, so it will not be necessary to stop the press for stock loading soon after the run has been started.

Watch the press all during operation. It is desirable to use a minimum of ink and moisture consistent with good clear reproduction. After runing about 100 copies, the ratchet control lever on the moistening fountain roller can be moved slightly to the right of a vertical position. Printed copies are carefully examined for ink distribution. Minor adjustment of the ink fountain adjusting screws may be necessary. It may be possible to re-

8-44. Set counter

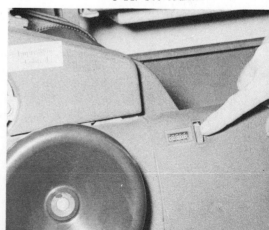

8-45. Variable speed control

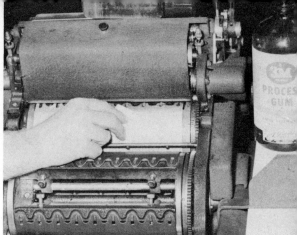

8-46. Gum the plate

duce the amount of ink being fed to the ink rollers—or it may be necessary to increase the flow of ink. However, when making a change in the ink fountain adjusting screws, the movement must be slight, and it requires from twenty to sixty impressions to be noticeable.

The variable speed control (8-45) can be adjusted for press operation speeds from 3,000 to 6,000 impressions per hour. It is recommended to run all paper or plastic plates at slow speed as well as starting all other types of plates at slow speed. Metal plates may be run at full speed after the run has been started. If difficulties with either the feeder or delivery develop, reduce the press speed until the difficulties have been corrected.

Cleaning The Press

After the run has been completed,

to clean the plate, place about ten sheets of scrap stock in the feeder. Run them through the press with the press "on" impression. This removes excess ink from the plate. Remove all stock from the press delivery so it will not become soiled during the clean-up.

Give the plate a thin coat of process gum (8-46). Remove the plate from the press and store in a suitable place. Moisten a wiping cloth with a solvent and wash both the plate cylinder and the blanket cylinder.

Remove the fountain solution container from the press (8-47). With sponge, remove the remaining fountain solution from the fountain.

Place several layers of newspapers on the press delivery, under the inking mechanism. Using an ink knife, remove the remainder of the ink from the ink fountain (8-48). The ink

8-47. Remove fountain solution container

8-48. Remove ink from fountain

8-49. Remove ink fountain from press

fountain roller is a composition, so be careful not to cut the roller with the ink knife.

Tilt the ink fountain so the adjusting screws will be upward (8-49). In

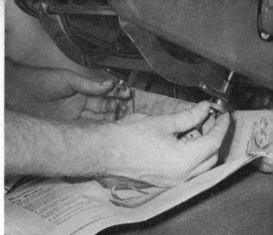

8-52. Raise wash-up attachment

this position, the fountain can be lifted straight up to remove it from the press. Place ink fountain on work bench for cleaning.

With the index finger of each hand, release the latch on each side of the ink ductor roller. Lift the roller from the press with the second finger of each hand (8-50). Place ink ductor roller on work bench with the ink fountain.

The ink wash-up attachment (8-51) is a rubber squeegee attached to a frame with a small tray designed to catch the ink and solvent squeegeed from the ink rollers.

On each side, at the lower end of the wash-up attachment frame are two thumbscrews. Tighten these until a light contact is made between the squeegee and the press roller (8-52). The rubber blade is flexible; therefore too much pressure folds it over,

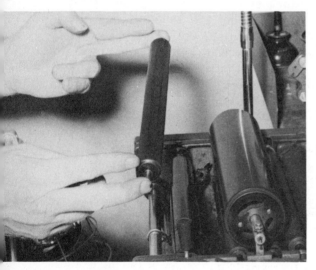

8-50. Remove ink fountain ductor roller

8-51. Wash-up attachment

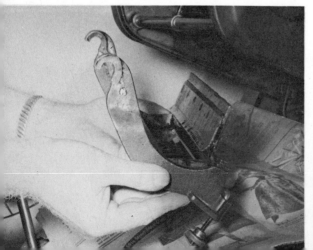

8-53. Apply solvent to press rollers

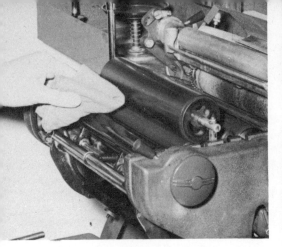

8-54. Wash ink fountain roller

8-55. Wash fountain and ductor roller

making it impossible to do a good cleaning job.

With the press on slow speed, squirt solvent on the large upper ink distribution roller (8-53). This usually has to be repeated in order to get the ink rollers thoroughly clean. Check the cleaning action of the wash-up attachment. It may be necessary to increase pressure of the wiper blade by turning the thumbscrews slightly. When a squeak develops, lower the wash-up attachment. The wash-up attachment should be removed from the press and cleaned about every other day.

Moisten a wiping cloth with solvent and wash the ink fountain roller (8-54). Be sure to clean the ends of the roller by holding the wiping cloth against them, turning the roller with the handwheel.

Wash the ink fountain and the ink ductor roller (8-55). Replace the ductor roller on the press; then return the ink fountain to the press.

Raise the lever on the far side of the press to disengage the form rollers from contact with the distribution rollers. Then raise the large ink distribution roller on top of the press so it is not in contact with the smaller distribution rollers below it.

Printing Paper Plates

The procedure in press preparation is the same for all kinds of plates. However, before installing a paper plate on the press, it is advisable to pre-damp the plate *before* it is placed on the press.

Press Adjustments

It is recommended that the manufacturer's operating manual be consulted before making adjustments other than those for normal operation.

Sample Tests—Chapter 8

Completion

Example: 1. Lithography is a planographic printing process.

1. Photographic plates are made from _____.

2. Lithographic printing refers to printing _____ from a lithographic plate.

3. Fountain solution is used to _____ the printing plate.

4. The ink _____ roller transfers ink from the fountain roller to the distribution rollers.

5. A coating of _____ _____ protects a plate while it is being handled or stored.

Multiple Choice

Example: <u>a</u> 1. Lithographic plates are dampened with (a) turpentine (b) water (c) fountain solution.

_____ 6. In offset lithography, (a) the image is printed directly from plate to paper (b) the image is transferred to rubber blanket, then to the paper, (c) the image is transferred from the blanket to the plate, and from the plate to the paper.

_____ 7. The lithographic plate should be moistened (a) before ink is applied (b) after ink has been applied (c) before the ink has been applied and continuously while ink is being applied.

_____ 8. The lithographic principle was discovered in 1798 by (a) Alois Senefelder (b) Benjamin Franklin (c) Johann Gutenberg.

_____ 9. While adjusting the ink fountain (a) the ductor roller should contact the distribution rollers (b) the distribution rollers should contact the fountain roller (c) the ductor roller should contact the fountain roller.

_____10. The head margin is adjusted on the press (a) by moving the plate on the plate cylinder (b) by moving the plate cylinder in relation to the blanket cylinder (c) by moving the blanket cylinder in relation to the impression cylinder.

Matching

Example: <u>a</u> 1. Motor   a. Switch

_____11. Plate protector   a. Flat

_____12. Platemaking   b. Fountain

_____13. Ink distribution

_____14. Blanket   c. Process gum

_____15. Wash-up attachment   d. Clean rollers

       e. Rubber

True-False

Example: T (F) 1. A lithographic plate should be inked before it has been dampened.

T F 16. The handwheels on a model 1250 Multilith press may be turned in either direction.

T F 17. After the ink fountain has been set, there will be sufficient ink on the ductor roller to ink the press.

T F 18. The gum should be removed from a metal plate before it is installed on the press.

T F 19. When the ink fountain adjusting screws are turned counterclockwise, the flow of ink is reduced.

T F 20. A paper plate should be predampened before being installed on the press.

Chapter 9

INTAGLIO PRINTING

THE INTAGLIO printing process is the opposite of relief printing, which uses a raised surface. In intaglio printing, the design is engraved or etched below the surface.

Commercial Application

Perhaps the most familiar product of the intaglio printing process is the rotogravure section found in many Sunday newspapers. Gravure printing, because of its versatility and flexibility in being able to print on any kind of surface such as foil, plastics, glassine, paper board or cloth, and with various types of inks, has made great inroads on letterpress and offset printing in the packaging and publication industry in recent years.

Intaglio plates that are used for most commercial printing are made by transferring the design to copper plates photographically. The design is then etched in the copper plate.

"Dry-point" is a term used to describe a method of making an intaglio plate by hand, using a needle or other sharp instrument.

Metal Plates

Artists frequently make plates by coating a thin sheet of engravers zinc or copper with an acid resist. The design is scratched through the acid resist, exposing the bare metal of the plate. The plate is then placed in an acid bath, which etches the design into the metal. When a suitable depth has been reached, the plate is removed from the bath, washed in water, and the acid resist removed.

The artist then may touch up weak spots in the plate, using engraving tools, after the design is etched into the plate.

Plastic Plates

Excellent results for a limited number of prints can be had from making intaglio plates from plastic material. Polished vinylite .015 inch in thickness makes an excellent plate. A phonograph needle clamped in a pin vise makes a suitable tool for engraving or incising the plate.

Plastic dry-point plates are recommended for beginning students for several reasons. First, the plate is transparent, so that the original design may be placed under it, making it visible on the surface of the plate to be engraved. Second, no strong acids are required, removing a hazard for younger students. Third, the materials are inexpensive and the design is more easily engraved.

9-1. Attach design to plate

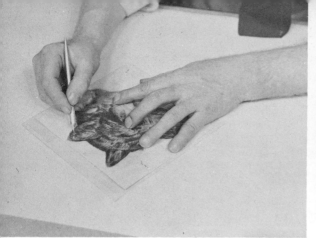

9-2. Engrave design in plate

9-3. Reduce printer's ink

The Design

Choose a design that will lend itself to line reproduction. When the design has been made, attach it to a piece of plastic which is about 1 inch larger than the design (9-1).

Engraving the Plate

Engrave the design in the plate, using a phonograph needle in a pin vise (9-2). The darker areas are engraved by incising lines in the plate close together. The closer the lines are engraved, the darker the area will reproduce. Crosshatched lines are used to reproduce shaded areas. In very light areas, the crosshatched lines are engraved farther apart than in the darker areas. The depth of engraving may vary from .002 of an inch to over .005 of an inch. To a limited extent, the deeper a line is engraved, the darker it will reproduce. It is recommended that you experiment with small, simple designs to become familiar with the techniques required to produce various effects.

Inking The Plate

Standard printer's ink, reduced with oil, may be used for inking the plate. Place a small quantity of ink, and a small quantity of oil, on a sheet of glass. With the index finger, mix a smaller quantity of ink and oil (9-3).

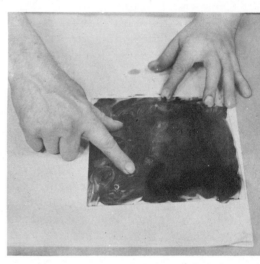

9-4. Ink the plate

Reduce the consistency of the ink to about one-third.

With the index finger, rub the reduced ink into the engraved lines of the plate (9-4). It is important to work the ink into every depression.

9-5. Wipe plate with paper pad

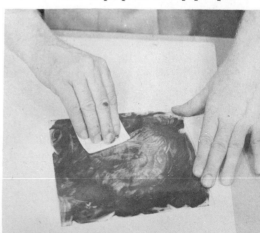

120

Fold a piece of paper, such as a paper hand towel, into a neat pad about 2 inches square. Wipe the entire plate to remove the ink from the non-printing areas (9-5).

After this initial wiping, do the final wiping with the heel of the hand (9-6). In wiping the plate, work at right angles to the engraved lines as much as possible.

Printing The Plate

Prints may be made either directly from the plate to paper, or they may be made indirectly by first printing on a rubber blanket, then transferring the print to the paper. The latter is recommended for making dry point prints from plastic plates. A proof press or other similar press may be used for making the impression. If an ordinary proof press is used, it is necessary to build up the bed so that the thickness of the build-up, plus the rubber blanket, will be about .925 of an inch. Place the plate on the built-up bed; then place the rubber blanket over the plate (9-7). An offset press blanket may be used for this purpose.

The impression is made on the rubber blanket by rolling the cylinder over this assembly (9-8). After the impression has been made, lift the blanket from the plate, remove the plate, and in its place lay the sheet

9-7. Make print on rubber blanket

9-8. Make impression on rubber blanket

of paper to be printed.

Carefully place the rubber blanket, which has the impression from the plate, face down on the paper to be printed (9-9). Roll the cylinder over

9-6. Wipe plate with heel of hand

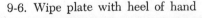

9-9. Transfer design from blanket to paper

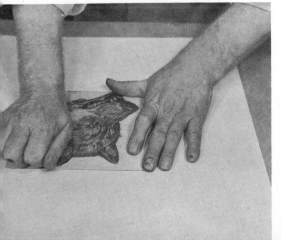

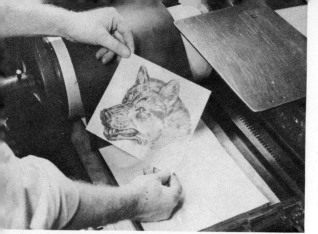

9-10. The printed design

the blanket, to transfer the design to the paper.

Examine the printed design (9-10). If the non-printing areas of the plate produce an undesired cast, it indicates the plate was not properly wiped. Generally, if the ink is too thick, it is difficult to wipe the plate perfectly clean in the non-printing area. If the image is light, and not clear, it is possible that the ink was too thin. Several experiments may be required for you to become familiar with the best ink consistency, as well as the techniques of wiping the plate. After examining the first print, it is not unusual to discover engraved areas that need to be touched up. Use a solvent to clean the plate and the blanket before making the next print.

It is possible to reproduce two or more colors from one inking of the plate. This requires careful inking and careful wiping of the plate.

Sample Tests—Chapter 9

Completion

Example: 1. Intaglio is the ___opposite___ of relief printing.

1. The design for dry-point should be of a type that will lend itself to _____ reproduction.

2. The closer the lines are incised in a dry-point plate, the _____ the area will reproduce.

3. Crosshatched lines are used to reproduce _____ _____.

4. Printer's ink reduced with _____ may be used for inking dry point plates.

5. After wiping the dry point plate with a paper pad, the final wiping should be done with the _____ of the hand.

Multiple Choice

Example: __b__ 1. Plastic dry-point plates should be engraved with (a) acid (b) a sharp pointed instrument (c) engraving tools.

_____ 6. If the non-printing areas of a dry-point plate produces an un-desired cast, it indicates that (a) too much ink was placed on the plate (b) too little ink was placed on the plate (c) the plate was improperly wiped.

_____ 7. If ink mixed for dry-point plates is too thick (a) it will be difficult to ink the plate (b) it will be difficult to wipe the plate (c) the lines will be too dark.

_____ 8. If the printed image is too light and not clear, it is possible that (a) the ink was too heavy (b) the plate was not properly wiped (c) the ink was too thin.

_____ 9. The design is transferred to the dry-point plate by (a) attaching the design to the plate (b) tracing the design on the plate (c) making the original design on the plate.

_____10. The initial wiping of the dry-point plate should be done (a) with a wiping cloth (b) a paper towel pad (c) the heel of the hand.

Matching

Example: <u>a</u> 1. Reduce ink a. Oil

_____11. Engrave
         plate

_____12. Indirect
         printing

_____13. Ink plate

_____14. Crosshatched
         lines

_____15. Plastic

a. Rubber
   blanket

b. Shaded
   area

c. Index finger

d. Transparent

e. Phonograph
   needle

True-False

Example: (T) F 1. Plastic plates are transparent.

T F 16. Prints made from intaglio plates are recognized as being superior to any others in showing very fine detail.

T F 17. The printing surface is raised on intaglio plates.

T F 18. Rotogravure sections in Sunday newspapers are printed from intaglio plates.

T F 19. Dry-point plates may be made from copper and zinc as well as plastic.

T F 20. It is not possible to make prints directly from dry-point plates.

Chapter 10

BLOCK PRINTING is an old art that preceded the invention of movable type. It was first practiced in the Orient early in the eighth century, when wood blocks were carved and printed on paper made of bamboo fiber.

In the fourteenth century, this printing process was introduced in Europe. Hand carved wood blocks were first used to reproduce religious pictures illustrating the text which had been handwritten by the scribes. Later, a few lines of explanation were also engraved on the same block as the design. As this technique was perfected, full pages were carved, making it possible to print entire books from carved wood blocks. Some blocks were printed on vellum stock (lamb skin), although the majority were reproduced on crude handmade paper.

The "Biblica Pauperum," or the "Poor Man's Bible," is among the early books reproduced entirely from carved wood blocks.

After the invention of movable type by Johann Guttenberg in 1439, wood blocks were still popular as a medium to reproduce pictures and illustrations. But, since the text matter was more easily composed in type, pages were often printed from a combination of wood blocks and type assembled together.

Wood blocks are still being carved today for the reproduction of designs. However, linoleum blocks are more commonly used because they are easier to carve yet will withstand printing thousands of impressions. Rubber, mounted on a type high block, is also a popular medium for the reproduction of simple designs.

In commercial printing, the use of linoleum blocks is very limited. Zinc and copper plates are used almost exclusively. The design is made on paper, photographed, transferred to zinc or copper plates, then etched with acid in relief. This method not only is more economical, but it provides a superior printing surface, making it possible to reproduce finer lines and greater detail.

Block cutting is still a popular activity in art classes, industrial arts classes, and in the hobby shop. It provides an inexpensive medium for individual expression that can be extremely attractive and useful in making multiple copies.

The Design

In preparation of a design for block printing, the principles of balance, emphasis, continuity, and contrast are all-important. Since the original design must be transferred to the block, it is desirable to make the design on transparent paper such as tracing paper used for drafting purposes.

Characteristics and limitations of the medium are important. Linoleum does not have a perfectly smooth surface. In order to reproduce an absolute solid, it is necessary to make the surface smooth. This can be done by scraping the surface with a razor blade or extremely fine sandpaper such as the kind used by photoengravers. Light lines or small dots in relief are not suited for reproduction from linoleum blocks because they have a tendency to break down under impression. Gradation of tone is practical only to a limited extent because this effect must be accomplished by a series of lines or dots very close together in the dark areas, gradually becoming finer and further apart in the lighter areas. Large areas of flat masses are most conducive to reproduction from linoleum blocks.

There are two basic methods of reproducing a given design. With one method, the design is cut in relief on the block; when it is printed, the stock provides the background for the design. With the other method, the design is incised in the block which leaves the background in relief; when it is printed, the design is actually the color of the stock, and the block print becomes the background for the design. In the parlance of the printer, this is referred to as a reverse plate. Study the design to determine the best method for reproduction. Generally, fine lines are best reproduced by incising them into the block.

Transferring the Design to Block

Linoleum is usually waxed. Remove this wax with a solvent, scrape it off, or use scouring powder. It is almost impossible to transfer a design to a waxed surface.

Since the block will print directly on the paper, the design must be cut in reverse; therefore place the design face down on the block. If the original

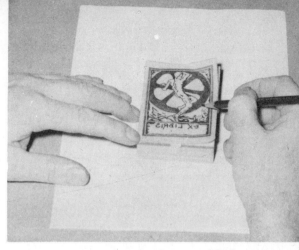

10-1. Transfer design to block

design is made on transparent paper, place a piece of carbon paper over the block, then the design face down on the carbon paper. Tape this assembly to the block so it will not move (10-1). The design can now be traced onto the block.

Designs made with a soft lead pencil can be placed face down on the block and taped in place. The design is transferred by rubbing the back of the paper, which forces some of the loose lead from the design to the block.

When more than one color appears in a design, cut one block for each color to be printed. The design for the key or master block is usually transferred as described above.

When using a black and white block as the basis for a color print, the offset method provides a simple yet accurate way of transferring the key block design to the new block. Ink the key design block and make an impression on a rubber blanket (10-2). A discarded offset press blanket works very well for this purpose.

Carefully place the block to be cut over the design printed on the rubber blanket (10-3). Slide this into the press to make an impression. If a press is not available, hand pressure on the block will transfer the design.

10-2. Print key block on rubber blanket

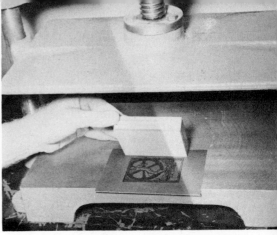

10-3. Offset design from blanket to block

Frequently the design transferred to the block is not perfect in every detail. Examine the transfer carefully and touch up any area which is not clear (10-4).

Carving the Block

Elaborate tools are not required for carving linoleum blocks. A sharp knife or a razor blade in a suitable holder will be adequate for many designs. Inexpensive cutters designed for cutting linoleum blocks are available at most art stores. Standard engraving tools are usually available in most school graphic arts centers.

A recommended set of engraving tools would include the following: ¼₄″ veining tool, ⅛″ gouge, ³⁄₁₆″ gouge, ¼″ gouge, and a small knife (10-5).

Regardless of the tools used, they must be sharp. First, outline the de-sign with the V-shaped veining tool, making a shallow V-cut which will establish the outlines of the printing face of the block. In the absence of a veining tool, the same result can be had by outlining the design with a sharp knife. Hold the knife at a slight angle so as to provide a taper from the printing surface outward to the base of the linoleum.

After the design has been outlined on the block, use a suitable gouge to remove the larger portions that are to be cut away (10-6). Non-printing areas immediately adjacent to the printing surface might be shallow; however, non-printing areas further from the printing surface must be cut deeper.

Extreme care must be exercised in cutting the block because it is not practical to fill in an area if the knife slips. A bench hook (10-7) is useful

10-4. Design transferred to block

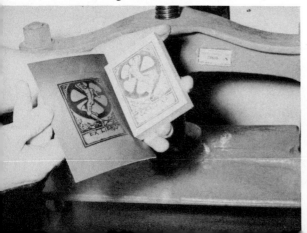

10-5. Engraving tools

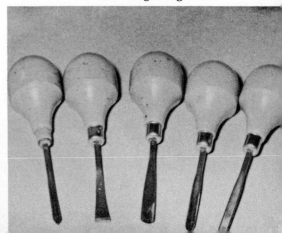

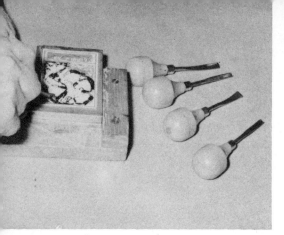

10-6. Cutting linoleum block

in holding the block while cutting. The knife or gouge must always be pushed away from the body, and, if a hand is used to hold the block, the knife or gouge must always be pushed away from the hand.

The block is cut in a manner that will provide a bevel from the printing surface outward to the base of the linoleum (10-8). If the printing surface is undercut, it will break down very easily and will not reproduce a sharp edge.

After the block has been cut and a proof taken (10-9), it is not unusual to discover several areas that need to be touched up and improved.

Printing The Block

Block prints are made by inking the block, then applying pressure to the paper stock. A platen press is usually most satisfactory to print the block, although other methods might be employed.

Blocks to be printed on a platen press must be .918″ or type high, and the block itself should be square. This is especially important where linoleum blocks are combined with type. The block must not be warped.

In order to print linoleum blocks satisfactorily on a platen press, the area of the block must not exceed more than one half the area of the

10-7. Hold block with bench hook

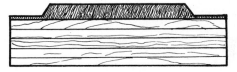

10-8. Cut bevel away from printing surface

press. For example, a 10 x 15 press has an area of 150 square inches. The block to be printed on the press must not exceed 75 square inches. See Chapter III.

Printer's ink can be used for printing linoleum blocks. However, in

10-9. Take proof of block

printing large solid areas, it may be necessary to reduce the ink with a few drops of thin varnish. Usually this will overcome the problem of the paper sticking to the block after an impression has been made.

In reproducing more than one

color, each color block must register perfectly with the prints of colors previously impressed. Therefore care must be given to placing paper and block in the correct position for each color run.

Sample Tests—Chapter 10

Completion

Example: 1. Block printing preceded the invention of _movable_ type.

1. Block printing was first practiced in the _____ early in the eighth century.
2. Hand carved wood blocks were first used to reproduce _____ _____.

3. Linoleum blocks are more commonly used today than wood blocks because they are _____ _____.
4. Designs for block cutting should be prepared on _____ paper.
5. When a design is cut in relief on a linoleum block, the _____ provides the background for the design.

Matching

Example: _a_ 1. Early books   a. Carved wood blocks

_____ 6. Transfer design   a. Offset transfer
_____ 7. Key block   b. Veining tool
_____ 8. Cutting block   c. Shallow cut
_____ 9. Near printing surface   d. Carbon paper
_____ 10. Push away from hand   e. Knife or gouge

True-False

Example: ⓣ F 1. The "Poor Man's Bible" is among the early books reproduced from wood blocks.

T F 11. After the invention of movable type, pages were often printed from a combination of wood blocks and type assembled together.
T F 12. Linoleum has a perfectly smooth surface.
T F 13. Fine lines are most easily cut in relief on linoleum blocks.
T F 14. Wax should be removed from the linoleum before the design is transferred.
T F 15. Designs on linoleum blocks must be cut in reverse.

Chapter 11

PHOTOGRAPHY is the art of producing images on sensitized surfaces by the action of light.

A source of light, such as the sun, illuminates the subject, which in turn reflects light through a small opening in the camera (a dark box), which excludes all light except that admitted by the small opening. A shutter, which might be compared to a door, regulates the length of time that the light is allowed to pass through the opening onto the back of the camera.

Film is a light-sensitive material which is placed in the back of the camera where the light rays converge. When the film is "exposed," light is reflected from the subject through the small opening in the camera, to the film (11-1).

11-1. Light is reflected from subject to film

The film is a transparent celluloid material which has been coated with a light-sensitive emulsion. When exposed, the emulsion begins to harden.

Light areas in the subject reflect more light than dark areas, and therefore the degree to which the sensitive emulsion is hardened will affect the density of certain areas. The image of the subject photographed is not visible on the film until after it has been developed. This is referred to as a latent image.

The film is placed in a developer which can discriminate between the exposed grains and the unexposed grains in the light-sensitive emulsion on the film.

The stop bath neutralizes the developer and stops the action at the desired stage of development. Examine several negatives from which good prints have been made to use as a guide in determining what constitutes a desirable general density of a properly developed film.

To make a print, the negative is placed in contact with light-sensitive photographic paper and exposed to light. The photographic paper is then developed, fixed, washed, and dried, resulting in a positive print of the negative.

A camera is a device used to expose film in taking a picture. Basically, it is a lightproof box with a small, glass-covered aperture (lens) that can be opened and closed (with a shutter). There is provision for securing the

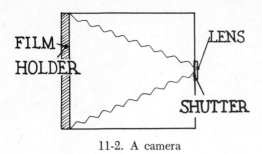

11-2. A camera

11-4. Install shutter

film at the back of the camera (film holder—11-2).

This description of our simplest camera is basic for all cameras. However, cameras in general use are considerably more elaborate and are actually very fine, delicate instruments. Devices for holding the film, adjustable distance between lens and film, quality and size of lens, viewing devices, and automatically timed shutter action synchronized with flash guns are the refinements which account for the wide range in the cost and value of cameras.

To Make a Simple Camera

A simple camera can be constructed from a one pound coffee can. No lens is used in this camera; however, a small pinhole admits the light rays. Normal exposure time must be increased because less light is admitted in the same length of time through the pinhole than would be transmitted through a lens. Also the points of light are more accurately transmitted by a lens, to produce a sharper and more well defined image on the film.

Since the inside of a coffee can is shiny, paint it, including the lid, with a flat black paint. This will prevent reflections of light within the camera.

Make a pinhole in the center of the bottom of the can (11-3).

Paste a black paper flap to the bottom of the can in such a way that the flap can be raised and lowered over the pinhole (11-4).

With masking tape, fasten a cardboard rectangle inside the cover of the coffee can. The cardboard is slightly larger than the film to be used. Note that the "top" end is parallel with the lettering on the outside of the can. Attach to the cardboard "art corners" commonly used to

11-3. Make pinhole in bottom

11-5. Make film holder inside cover

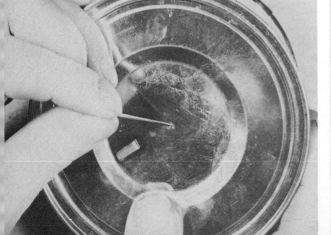

11-6. Completed camera

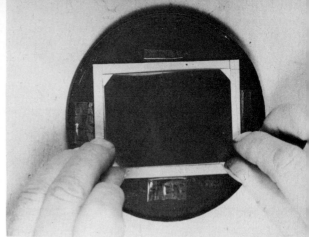

11-7. Place film in holder

mount photographs in albums, or with tape and paper make a similar device to hold the film on each corner (11-5). The cardboard provides a surface on which the film can be attached and kept flat.

The completed camera (11-6) is the simplest and most inexpensive device there is for making a satisfactory photograph.

To Take a Picture

In *total darkness,* and with *clean dry hands,* place a sheet of 2½ x 3½ inch film in the film holder on the coffee can lid. Hold the sheet film so the notch is in the *lower right hand* corner; in this position the emulsion will be up. Handle the film by the edges to avoid finger marks. Place the lid tightly on the coffee can.

The camera must be held perfectly still on its side and with the lettering *up* on the can. A stepladder or similar rigid support must be used to keep the camera from moving. Point the camera at the subject and lift the shutter, holding it up for a length of time which is recommended for the film being used (11-8). For the average subject in bright sunlight, exposure will be about 1 second for fast sheet film; 4 to 6 seconds for regular sheet film.

11-8. Taking a picture

To Develop Film

To illustrate developing film and making a print, use chemicals recommended for the film. One pack provides the chemicals needed to process fifty 2½ x 3½ inch prints or their equivalent.

11-9. Mix chemicals

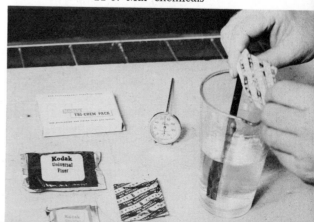

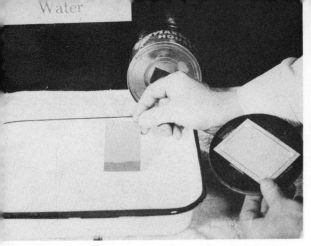

11-10. Place film in water

11-11. Place film in developer

Mix the developer, stop bath, and fixer according to directions received with each chemical pack (11-9). Follow instructions of the manufacturer, not only in regard to mixing the chemicals, but also in their use when processing film or prints, if they vary from the directions that follow. Since the same chemicals may be used for making prints and developing additional film, store the chemicals in dark brown bottles to protect the contents from light. Bottles of this type may be obtained at local drug stores at nominal cost. Always plainly mark the contents of chemical mixtures stored in each bottle.

Films may be developed either by the tray method or by the tank method. The tray method has been illustrated because no special equipment other than porcelain trays or glass cake pans are required. The same procedure is used for the tank method, although it is advisable to use a special film holder to hold the film in the tanks. The tanks are made especially for this purpose and can be obtained from most photographic supply houses. A standard photographic timing device was used here, although a luminous dial watch or other timing device could have been substituted.

In total darkness, place the film in a tray of water for about a minute (11-10).

In total darkness, transfer the film from the tray of water into the tray of developer for 3½ minutes. The developer is kept at 68° F. (11-11).

In total darkness, remove the film from the developer. Let the excess developer drain from the film for about 2 seconds. Then place the film in the stop bath for 15 seconds.

11-12. Place film in stop bath

11-13. Place film in fixer

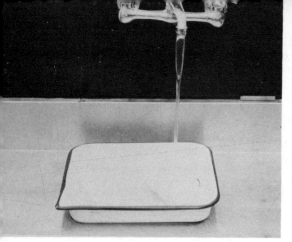

11-14. Wash in cool water

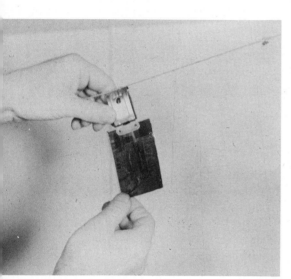

11-15. Dry film

In total darkness, drain excess stop bath from the film for 2 seconds; then place film in the fixer. After about 1 minute, the room light can be turned on. Continue to fix the film for twice

11-17. Cut opening in mask

the time it takes to remove the milky appearance (11-13).

When the film is fixed, wash it in a tank of cool running water for at least 20 minutes (11-14).

Wipe the film with a clean photographers sponge and hang it up to dry (11-15).

To Make Prints

Use the same developer, stop bath, and fixer previously prepared for developing film.

On a sheet of opaque paper large enough to cover the ground glass on the printing box, mark the size of prints to be made (11-16).

Carefully cut the opening in the mask, the size of the print to be made (11-17).

Position the negative under the opening in the mask with the emulsion (dull) side upward (11-18).

11-16. Prepare mask

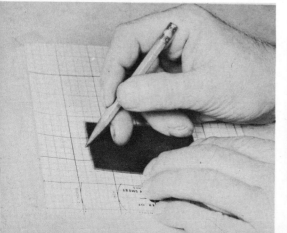
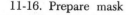

11-18. Locate negative under mask

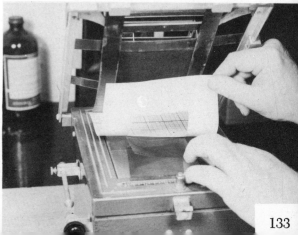

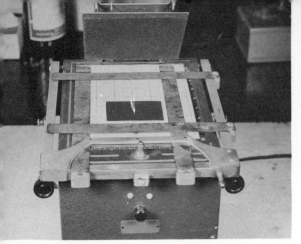

11-19. Adjust guides for paper

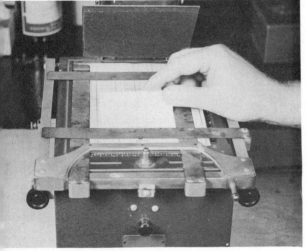

11-20. Position printing paper

Lower the guides for positioning the printing paper. Adjust these so an even margin will be maintained on two edges. The printing paper can then be positioned to the corner formed by the two guides (11-19).

11-21. Close printing frame

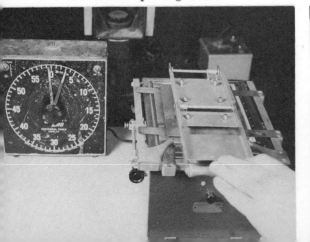

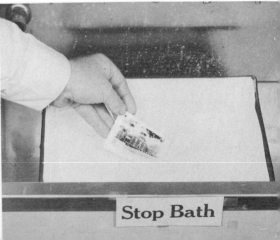

11-22. Place exposed paper in developer

Under a *safelight,* the package of printing paper may be opened. With *clean, dry hands,* position the printing paper to the guides with the emulsion (shiny) side downward (11-20). A safelight is a dim, colored light which will not affect the printing paper. An ordinary 7½ watt red light is satisfactory.

Close the printing frame (11-21). Expose the average negative for 3 seconds. If the resulting print is too light, increase the exposure time; if the print is too dark, decrease the exposure time.

The developer is at 68° F. Use the *safelight.* Place the exposed paper in the developer for 1 minute with continuous agitation (11-22).

Use the *safelight.* Immerse the print in the stop bath for 5 to 10 seconds with continuous agitation (11-23).

11-23. Place print in stop bath

11-24. Place print in fixer

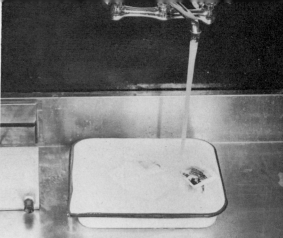

11-25. Wash prints

Fix the print for about 5 to 10 minutes. Agitate the print when it is first placed in the fixer and at frequent intervals thereafter, to insure complete fixing and to avoid stains (11-24).

After fixing the print, wash it in a large tray of cool running water for at least an hour (11-25). Prints which are not thoroughly washed will turn yellow or brown in a short time.

When the prints have been thoroughly washed, lift them from the water by one corner to drain off the excess water. For a gloss print, roll washed prints on a clean Ferrotype tin. Let prints dry at room temperature; remove from the plate, starting with the corner of the print (11-26). Prints may also be dried between blotters, which will give a matte (dull) finish.

If a commercial printing box similar to the one used in the illustrations is not available, other devices could be used for printing pictures. It is necessary to bring the negative and printing paper in contact with each other and to have a source of light which will expose the photographic paper through the negative. The negative, mask, and printing paper could be held in contact between two ordinary pieces of glass. An ordinary in-

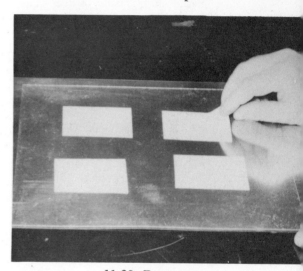

11-26. Dry prints

candescent light could be used to make the exposure. With this arrangement, it would be necessary to experiment to find the most suitable exposure time. If the resulting print is too light, it can be corrected either by increasing the exposure time, increasing the size of the light bulb, or bringing the source of light closer to the exposure frame. If the resulting print is too dark, it can be corrected either by decreasing the exposure time, decreasing the size of the light bulb, or moving the source of light further from the exposure frame.

A dark room is necessary to make this activity practical in the school shop.

Sample Tests—Chapter 11

Completion

Example: 1. Photography is the art of producing images on sensitized surfaces by the action of <u>light</u>.

1. The shutter of a camera regulates the length of time that _____ is allowed to pass through the lens.
2. Film is a light-sensitive material which is placed in the back of the camera where the light rays _____.

3. The image of the subject photographed is not visible on the film until after it has been developed; this is referred to as a _____.
4. The stop bath _____ the developer and stops the action at the desired stage of development.
5. A camera is a device used to _____ film in taking a picture.

Matching

Example: <u>a</u> 1. Light-sensitive a. Film

_____ 6. Light areas   a. Lens

_____ 7. Dark areas   b. Develop film

_____ 8. Camera   c. Reflect more light

_____ 9. Total darkness   d. Density

_____10. Negative   e. Reflect less light

True-False

Example: Ⓣ F 1. The quality of the lens will affect the value of a camera.

T F 11. A pinhole camera should be held close to the body to minimize movement while taking a picture.
T F 12. The film must be transferred from the camera to film holder for developing in total darkness.
T F 13. The temperature of the developer should be 78° F.
T F 14. Film being developed should be placed in the stop bath before it is placed in the fixer.
T F 15. A printed picture which is too light indicates that the printing exposure time was too long.

Chapter 12

LIKE MANY phases of the graphic arts, papermaking has a fascinating history. It begins shortly after the death of Christ.

Ts'ai Lun, a young Chinese scholar, is credited with being the first man to make a fair grade of paper as early as 105 A.D. It is assumed that he used a mixture of bamboo fiber, old rags, and the inner fibers of the mulberry tree. He beat the ingredients into a mass, mixed it with water, and poured it onto grass molds. The excess water seeped through the grass mat and left a flat film of matted fiber. This was dried in the sun, then rubbed with a stone to make the surface smooth.

When the Arabs conquered Samarkand, which was at the western limits of Chinese culture, they learned the art of making paper from the Chinese prisoners of war. This art rapidly spread to Northern Africa, Europe, England and, in the seventeenth century, was introduced in America.

In 1798, a Frenchman named Louis Robert announced that he had discovered a way for making paper continuously. He secured a patent for his machine, but he did not have adequate funds to finance its manufacture. Two wealthy London stationers, Henry and Sealy Fourdrinier, undertook its manufacture and in 1804 the first machine for making paper continuously was placed in operation. The machine was named the Fourdrinier machine after the two men who developed Louis Robert's invention. While the present-day paper-

making machine has been changed somewhat in its details, it is fundamentally the same machine.

Handmade Paper

Making paper by hand is an ideal way to become familiar with the basic principles of papermaking. It is rather simple, and does not require extensive equipment.

An ordinary tub, a mold consisting of a frame covered with a fine-mesh copper screen, and a deckle, which is a simple frame that fits over the mold, make up the basic equipment (12-1).

Fill the tub about ¾ full of warm water. Shred about forty sheets of a soft tissue into the water (12-2). Soft tissue is a substitute for pulp. Frequently, dried pulp can be secured from a paper mill.

Stir this mixture until the tissue dissolves in the water (12-3).

Boil two tablespoons of laundry

12-1. Paper making equipment

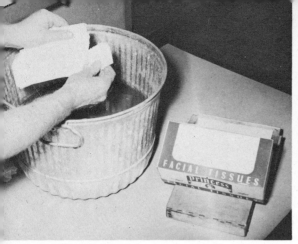

12-2. Shred tissue in tub of water

12-3. Stir mixture

12-4. Add starch

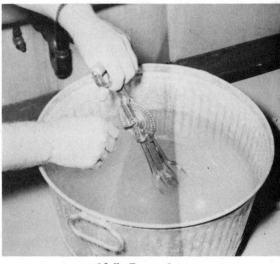

12-5. Beat mixture

starch in two cups of water. This is sufficient to prepare about 4 gallons of water. Add this mixture to the warm water in the tub (12-4).

With an ordinary egg beater or a wire spoon, thoroughly beat this mixture until it is free of lumps and has a milky appearance (12-5).

Place the deckle over the mold (with the deckle up); then slide the

12-6. Insert mold and deckle

12-7. Lift deckle and mold

12-8. Remove deckle from mold

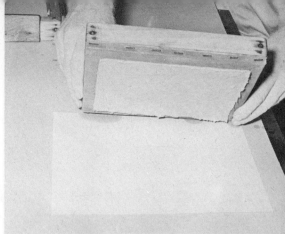

12-9. Place mold on damp blotting paper

12-10. Raise mold

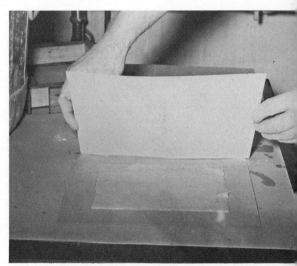

12-11. Place blotter over sheet formed

assembly into the mixture at a slight angle, slowly bringing the deckle and mold into a level position (12-6).

Lift the deckle and mold from the mixture. *Keep it level* (12-7).

Place the mold on a table; then lift the deckle from the mold (12-8).

Place the mold on a sheet of damp blotting paper (12-9).

Gently raise the mold, which will leave the moist sheet of paper, just formed, on the blotting paper (12-10).

Place another sheet of blotting paper on top of the moist paper (12-11). This will absorb some of the excess water from the sheet.

If more than one sheet of paper is being made, interleave blotting paper between each sheet of paper formed. Place a smooth piece of pressed board on top of the pile, and weigh this

12-12. Place under weights

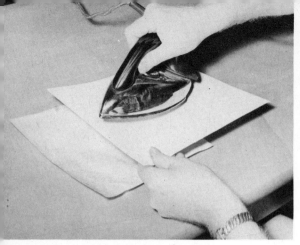

12-13. Press sheets dry

12-14. Sizing the sheet

12-15. Roll excess moisture from sheet

12-16. Press sheet

down so the sheets will dry under pressure (12-12).

After most of the moisture has been absorbed by the blotting paper, the sheet, although still wet, will be strong enough to be moved without support. Place the sheet on a hard surface, cover it with a dry blotter; then press until dry (12-13).

The paper at this point, although dry, is soft and absorbent. In order to harden the surface and to bind the fibers more firmly, the sheet should be sized. A satisfactory sizing solu-

tion can be made by mixing about 1½ ounces of bone glue in 1 pint of warm water. Soak this until soft, and stir until well dissolved. After adding a pint of cold water to the mixture, immerse the sheet of paper in it (12-14).

Remove the sheet from the sizing solution, placing it on a dry blotter. With a roller, squeeze out the excess moisture (12-15).

Place a smooth piece of paper on each side of the sized sheet; then press until dry (12-16).

Sample Tests—Chapter 12

Completion

Example: 1. Papermaking was introduced to America in the __17th__ Century.

1. Ts'ai Lun, a young Chinese scholar, is credited with being the first man to make a fair grade of paper as early as _____.

2. Ts'ai Lun dried his paper in the sun; then rubbed it with a stone to make it _____.

3. The Arabs learned the art of papermaking from _____ prisoners of war.

4. A papermaking _____ is a frame covered with a fine-mesh copper screen.

5. A satisfactory sizing solution for handmade paper can be made by mixing 1½ ounces of _____ _____ in 1 pint of water.

Matching

Example: <u>a</u>   1. Mold   a. Deckle

_____ 6. Papermaking machine

_____ 7. Harden surface

_____ 8. Inventor

_____ 9. Pulp

_____10. Remove moisture

a. Sizing

b. Fourdrinier

c. Louis Roberts

d. Blotter

e. Soft tissue

True-False

Example: Ⓣ F   1. Paper is made from plant fiber.

T   F   11. The first papermaking machine was named after its inventor.

T   F   12. Starch should be added to the mixture of dissolved tissue in a tub of water.

T   F   13. The mixture of water, dissolved tissue, and starch should be thoroughly mixed until it is free of lumps and has a milky appearance.

T   F   14. A sheet of paper can be lifted from the mold shortly after the sheet has been formed.

T   F   15. An ordinary clothes iron may be used to press handmade sheets of paper.

Chapter 13

THERE ARE three types of duplicators commonly used in modern offices for reproducing written and printed material. Although they are representative of graphic arts, they are not considered production machines, with which material is printed for sale in various forms. The product of these machines is generally used by the office in which it originates.

Yet, since they are machines used to reproduce printed material, a book on graphic arts would be incomplete without a brief explanation of these three basic processes.

Stencil Duplicator

The stencil duplicator employs a thin stencil through which ink is forced onto paper. The stencil is a fibrous, porous tissue which has been coated on both sides with a wax. This wax, when struck by the type of a typewriter, is forced aside. A stylus may also be used to force the wax aside, exposing the porous tissue which will permit ink to pass through like a sieve.

When the stencil has been completed, it is stretched around a perforated drum which contains a fluid ink. Paper to be printed passes under the perforated drum, and above an impression roller which holds the paper in firm contact with the drum. Paper is fed into the machine and, as the drum with the stencil attached rotates, the paper is positioned under the stencil. The ink is forced through the openings in the stencil onto the paper. The stencil is positioned to the paper vertically by adjusting the ink drum, and the lateral adjustment is made by positioning the paper to the stencil.

The Spirit Duplicator

Spirit duplicating is actually a planographic printing process. A master sheet is typewritten or drawn on, and receives a reversed impression on the back, from a carbon sheet attached.

13-1. Stencil duplicator

13-2. Spirit duplicator

After the master has been made, the carbon sheet is removed and the master is attached to the cylinder of the duplicator. As the cylinder is rotated, the sheet to be printed is fed into the machine passing under a felt pad moistened with a fluid which in turn slightly moistens the sheet. The paper passes under the cylinder to which the master is attached and is held in contact with the master by a composition impression roller. The fluid with which the sheet has been moistened is a solvent for the carbon deposited on the master. In this way, the moistened sheet picks up the carbon image from the master by dissolving a little of the carbon from the master which in turn adheres to the printed sheet.

Each sheet printed slightly reduces the carbon deposit on the master and after the carbon deposit gets thin, the printed copies become weaker in appearance. The number of good, legible copies that can be printed from one master is dependent upon the quality of the master. However, 300 are not unusual.

Different colored carbons are available, which makes it possible to print several colors on a sheet at one time. However, for each color printed, a separate carbon must be used to place the image on the master.

Photo-copying

Photo-copying machines are increasingly becoming commonplace in the modern office.

13-3. Photo-copying

These machines employ photographic principles, to reproduce direct copies of previously printed, typewritten, or written material. They are usually used for reproducing a limited number of reprints because, in comparison with other methods, the process is slow and the unit cost for each reproduction is relatively high. Much development is being done on photographic printing. For making a few copies, it is actually faster than setting up other types of duplicators.

Detailed Instructions

There are many different manufacturers of all three types of office duplicators. Different models are available: some are hand operated; some are power driven. It is recommended that instruction manuals prepared by the manufacturer be followed for each machine. Improvements in these machines have simplified their operation and a proficient operator can be trained in a very short time.

Sample Tests—Chapter 13

Completion

Example: 1. There are <u>three</u> types of duplicators which are commonly used in modern offices for duplicating written and printed material.

1. The _____ _____ employs a thin stencil through which ink is forced onto paper.
2. The _____ _____ is actually a planographic printing process.

3. On a spirit duplicator, the fluid with which the sheet has been moistened is a _____ for the carbon deposited on the master.
4. Photo-copying machines employ _____ _____ to reproduce direct copies of previously printed, typewritten, or written material.
5. The number of good, legible copies that can be printed from one master on a spirit duplicator is dependent upon the _____ of the master.

Matching

Example: <u>a</u> 1. Office machines   a. Duplicators

_____ 6. Perforated drum   a. Stylus

_____ 7. Spirit duplicator   b. Stencil

_____ 8. Drawings   c. Wax

_____ 9. Fibrous porous tissue   d. Carbon

_____10. Felt pad   e. Moisten sheet

True-False

Example: Ⓣ F 1. The product of duplicating machines is generally used in the office in which it originates.

T F 11. Stencils may be cut on a regular typewriter.

T F 12. On stencil duplicators, the stencil is positioned vertically by adjusting the ink drum.

T F 13. More than one color can be printed at the same time on a spirit duplicator.

T F 14. Over 1,000 good legible copies from one master on a spirit duplicator would not be unusual.

T F 15. The unit cost of reproductions from a photo-copying machine is high, but for its purpose compares with other methods of duplicating.

Selected Bibliography

Composition

Cleeton and Pitkin, *General Printing*, Mc-Knight & McKnight, Bloomington, Ill., 1935.

Hague, C. W., *Printing for the Schools*, Bruce Publishing Co., Milwaukee, Wis., 1943.

Hlasta, Stanley, *Printing Types and How To Use Them*, Rutgers University Press, 1950.

Oswald, John Clyde, *A History of Printing*, D. Appleton & Co., 1928.

Polk, Ralph W., *The Practice of Printing*, Chas. A. Bennett Co., Inc., Peoria, Ill., 1952.

Updike, Daniel B., *Printing Types*, Harvard University Press, Cambridge, Mass., 1937.

Presswork

Harrison, J. N., *Pressman's Pocket Manual*, Central Trade School, Oakland, Cal., 1942.

Hoch, Fred W., *Handbook for Pressmen*, Fred W. Hock Associates, Inc., 1946.

Polk, Ralph W., *Elementary Platen Presswork*, Chas. A. Bennett Co., Inc., 1955.

Spicher, Craig R., *The Practice of Presswork*, Published by Author, 1929.

Layout

DeLopatecki, Eugene, *Typographers Desk Manual*, Ronald Press Co., 1949.

Dwiggins, W. A., *Layout In Advertising*, Harper and Bros., 1948.

Felton, Charles J., *Layout*, Published by Author, 1949.

Friend and Hefter, *Graphic Design*, McGraw-Hill Book Co., 1936.

Karch, Randolph R., *Basic Lessons in Printing Layout*, Bruce Publishing Co., 1952.

McCullough, Wava, *Practical Layout*, Art Books For All, 1950.

Morrison, Stanley, *First Principles of Typography*, MacMillan Co., 1936.

Munsell, A. H., *Color Notation*, Munsel Color Co., 1941.

Sutton, Albert, *Design and Makeup of The Newspaper*, Prentice-Hall, Inc., 1948.

Silk Screen

Biegeleisen, J. I., and Busenbark, E. J., *The Silk Screen Printing Process*, McGraw-Hill Book Co., Inc., 1941.

Biegeleisen, J. I., *Silk Screen Stencil Craft As A Hobby*, Harper and Bros., 1939.

Eisenberg, James, *Silk Screen Printing*, McKnight and McKnight Pub. Co., 1952.

Kosloff, Albert, *Mitography*,

Screen Process Printing, Vocational Development Committee, Screen Process Printing Association, International, 1954.

Zahn, Bert, *Screen Process Methods of Reproduction*, Frederick J. Drake & Co., 1935.

Bookbinding

Cockerell, Douglas, *Bookbinding, and the Care of Books*, Pitman Pub. Corp., New York, Fifth Edition, 1953.

Davenport, Cyril, *The Book, Its History and Development*, Peter Smith, New York, 1930.

Groneman, Chris. H., *General Bookbinding*, McKnight & McKnight, Bloomington, Ill., 1946.

Hewitt-Bates, *Bookbinding for Schools*, Chas. A. Bennett Co., Inc., Sixth Edition, 1954.

Palmer, E. W., *Course in Bookbinding*, Employing Bookbinders of America, Inc., Revised Ed., 1950.

Pratt, Guy A., *Let's Bind A Book*, The Bruce Publishing Co., Milwaukee, Wis., 1940.

Smith, F. R., *Bookbinding*, Pitman Publishing Corporation, New York.

Photography

Photo Tips For Simple Cameras, Eastman Kodak Co., 1953.

Kodak School and Club Service, Eastman Kodak Co., 1954.

Some Chemical Reactions In Photography, Eastman Kodak Co.

The Brownie Book of Picture Taking, Eastman Kodak Co., 1955.

Developing, Printing, Enlarging, Eastman Kodak Co., 1955.

Planographic Printing

Carruzi, Richard T., *Offset Duplicator Techniques,* Harold L. Taylor, Inc., 1945.

Cumming, David, *Handbook of Lithography,* A. & C. Black, London, 1950.

Hock, Fred W. and Harris, Carl B., *Offset Duplicator Techniques,* Fred W. Hock, Associates, 1953.

Lithographic Technical Foundation, Inc., *LTF Shop Manuals,* Lithographic Technical Foundation, Inc., New York.

Sayer, I. H., *Photography and Platemaking For Photo-Lithography,* Lithographic Textbook Publishing Co., 1949.

Sayer, I. H., *The Single Color Offset Press,* Lithographic Textbook Publishing Company, 1948.

Soderstrom, Walter E., *The Lithographers Desk Manual,* Waltwin Publishing Co., 1951.

Block Cutting

Frankenfield, Henry, *Block Printing With Linoleum,* Hunt Pen Co., 1949.

George, Ross F., *Speedball Text Book,* Hunt Pen Co., 1946.

Kafka, Francis J., *Linoleum Block Printing,* McKnight & McKnight Pub. Co., 1955.

Rice, William S., *Block Prints And How To Make Them,* Bruce Pub. Co., 1941.

Miscellaneous

Alling, Joseph T., *Paper—A Brief Account of How It Is Made,* The Alling & Cory Co., 1924.

Auble, J. W., *Arithmetic for Printers,* Chas. A. Bennett Co., Inc., 1954.

Barry, John J., *How To Make Etchings,* Bridgeman Publishers, Inc., 1929.

Bennett, Colin N., *Elements of Photogravure,* American Photographic Publishing Co., 1935.

Cansler, Russell N., *Fundamentals of Mimeographing,* A. B. Dick Company, 1952.

Carter, T. F., *Invention of Printing In China and It's Spread Westward,* Columbia University Press, 1925.

Cartwright, C., *Photogravure,* American Photographic Publishing Co., 1939.

Clark, F. E., *Craftsmen in The Graphic Arts,* International Textbook Co., 1950.

Hunter, Dard, *Paper Making,* Alfred A. Knopf, 1943.

Karch, R. R., *Graphic Arts Procedures,* American Technical Society, 1948.

Karch, R. R., *How To Plan and Buy Printing,* Prentice-Hall Co., 1950.

Karch, R. R., *How To Recognize Type Faces,* McKnight & McKnight, 1952.

Kauffmann, Desire, *Graphic Arts and Crafts,* D. Van Nostrand Co., 1948.

Marinaccio, Anthony and Osburn, Burl N., *Exploring The Graphic Arts,* The Haddon Craftsmen, Inc., 1942.

How To Make Paper By Hand, Hammermill Paper Company, Erie, Pa., 1952.

Bronze Stamping Leaf, GPO-PIA Joint Research Bulletin, Bindery Series No. 4, U. S. Government Printing Office.

The Process of Marbling, GPO-PIA Joint Research Bulletin, Bindery Series No. 1, U. S. Government Printing Office.

INDEX

147